ELEMENTARY LOGIC

D. J. O'Connor PhD is Emeritus Professor of Philosophy at Exeter University. He has had varied teaching experience in universities in South Africa, Keele and Liverpool and as visiting professor at Brandeis and Pennsylvania Universities. His publications include *Introduction to Symbolic Logic* (with A. H. Basson), *John Locke*, *The Correspondence Theory of Truth* and various papers in philosophical journals.

Dr Powell is Senior Lecturer in Philosophy at Exeter University and has also been visiting professor at Washington and Toronto Universities. Her publications include *Knowledge of Actions* and various papers in philosophical journals.

TEACH YOURSELF BOOKS

ELEMENTARY LOGIC

D. J. O'Connor Ph.D and
Betty Powell Ph.D

TEACH YOURSELF BOOKS
Hodder and Stoughton

Published in the USA by David McKay & Co. Inc., 750 Third Avenue, New York, NY 10017, USA.

British Library C.I.P.

O'Connor, Daniel John
    Elementary logic. – (Teach yourself books).
    1. Logic
    I. Title   II. Powell, Betty   III. Series
    160 ·   BC108

    ISBN 0–340–25824–1

Printed and bound in Great Britain for Hodder and Stoughton paperbacks, a division of Hodder and Stoughton Ltd, Mill Road, Dunton Green, Sevenoaks, Kent, (Editorial Office: 47 Bedford Square, London, WC1B 3DP) by Richard Clay (The Chaucer Press) Ltd, Bungay, Suffolk

Contents

Preface

This book offers beginners to the subject a very simple introduction to modern logic. It is written chiefly for the benefit of those who have to study logic on their own or with little outside help. For that reason, explanations have been made as full as possible, particularly in the early stages of the book.

It cannot be emphasised too strongly that progress in logic depends on regular practice with exercises. There are more than 500 exercises in the book. Solutions are provided to all of them. We have tried to grade the exercises to the progress of the text.

The *Notes on Further Reading* will give help to those who wish to take their study of logic beyond the very elementary level reached in this book.

D. J. O'Connor
Betty Powell

Part I

1 The Logic of Statements (1)

In one sense, everyone who is at all likely to read this book is familiar with its subject matter. We are all, to a greater or lesser extent, familiar with arguments. By this, we do not mean that we have all, at some time or other, been involved in discussions or near-quarrels, although that is also true. But we have all put forward arguments; we have tried to establish conclusions by giving reasons. We are familiar with arguments presented by others. Some of these we accept as good ones and others we reject as bad ones. To use the technical terms, we accept some as valid and reject others as invalid. In many cases, we are right. We should be right to accept as valid (as a good one) the argument:

1 If you are going to Spain, you will need a passport. You are going to Spain. Therefore, you will need a passport.

We should be right to reject as invalid the argument:

2 If you are going to Spain you will need a passport. But you are not going to Spain. Therefore you will not need a passport.

Each of us is able to distinguish some valid arguments from

invalid ones, although, of course, some people are more able than others.

As one might expect, people who have more practice in assessing arguments are likely to be better at distinguishing valid from invalid ones. If we were to give a collection of arguments, ranging from very simple ones to very complex ones, and were to ask a number of people to say which were valid, most would get at least some right, and some people would get rather more right, although it is unlikely that anybody would get all right. That, however, is something we shall not do, for the very good reason that it is not enough simply to be able to see that an argument is valid. We need also to understand *why* it is valid.

Why should we be right to accept the first argument as valid, and reject the second argument as invalid? The short answer to this is that we should be right because the argument *is* valid. But why is it valid? What is it about this argument that makes it valid, and what is it about the second argument that makes it invalid? If you think for a moment, you will see that it will not do to say simply: 'Well, one can just see that it is.' For suppose that you 'just see' that a given argument is valid, and the next person 'just sees' that it is invalid. You cannot both be right. An argument cannot be both valid and invalid, any more than a simple sum in arithmetic can have an answer which is both right and wrong.

Throughout this book we shall be studying the ways in which valid arguments are distinguished from invalid ones. We shall, to begin with at any rate, be using as examples, simple arguments which you will probably be able to see intuitively ('just see') to be valid or invalid. But we shall be explaining the techniques by which it can be proved that these arguments are valid. We shall be applying the techniques of symbolic logic to arguments.

Symbols can be off-putting. If you turn to the latter sections of this book, you will find the exercises quite incomprehensible. But this is not surprising. You would not expect to be able to read passages in a foreign language until you had learned the rudiments of that language. If the language happened to be, say, Russian, you would not expect to be able to learn even the elementary bits until you had mastered the alphabet. Symbolic logic, as its name implies, uses symbols, and the student must learn these and learn to use them. They are not, however, very difficult and there are not very many of them. We shall introduce them gradually, and define them carefully. This, however, will not just be for the benefit of the beginner, but because of the nature of the subject. Each step follows from the last, and each symbol and technical term must be defined. Each step, although it may be simple, is essential, so please do not be tempted to skip over any bits.

Logic is a precise discipline, and so even in talking about our subject matter, in our case arguments, we must be as precise as possible. We must be a good deal more careful and in some matters, more accurate, than we are when we talk about arguments in ordinary, everyday discourse. Let us first, then, be more precise about arguments.

An argument consists of a set of one or more premisses, a conclusion, and some indication of which is the conclusion and which the premisses. Arguments can be presented in such a way that the conclusion is given last, but they can also be presented in such a way that the conclusion is given first. For example:

If Jones comes, then Smith will stay away. Jones will come. Therefore, Smith will stay away.

Here the conclusion is given last, and is signalled by the word 'therefore'. Other words which signal the conclusion of an argument are 'thus' and 'so'. But this very same argument could be written:

Smith will stay away; because Jones will come, and if Jones comes, then Smith will stay away.

Here the conclusion occurs first, and the premisses are signalled by the word 'because'.

Each of the premisses and the conclusion of an argument is a statement or proposition. There are good reasons, which fortunately we do not need to go into, for avoiding the term 'proposition'. On the other hand, we shall, in the early sections of this book, be working with what is known as the *Propositional Calculus*. We shall use the terms 'statement' and 'proposition' interchangeably.

A statement (or proposition) is, by definition, either true or false. The following are statements:

> Roses are red.
> Jones came.
>
> Roses are red and violets are blue.
> Either Jones came or Smith came.

The following are *not* statements:

> Oh!
> Damn!
> Why did that happen?
> Come again soon.

These are, respectively, an exclamation; an expletive; a question; and a request, or invitation. Such expressions cannot be true or false.

In an argument, the statements which are the premisses imply, or purport to imply, the statement which is the conclusion. When an argument is written with the conclusion last, we are saying, by the use of the word 'therefore', that the premisses imply the conclusion. When an argument is written with the conclusion first, it is claimed, by the use of the word 'because', that the conclusion is implied by the premisses. In an invalid argument, the premisses do not imply the conclusion, even though they purport to do so. In distinguishing between valid and invalid arguments we are distinguishing those arguments in which the premisses imply the conclusion, from those in which the premisses do not imply the conclusion.

To confuse truth with validity is a common mistake. One often hears people speak of 'valid' or 'invalid' statements when what they really mean is 'true' or 'false'. The statement

If wages rise, then inflation will increase

is either true or it is false, but it is neither valid nor invalid. Arguments are valid or invalid; they are not true or false. When we speak of an argument's being valid, we are saying something about the way in which the statements which constitute the premises are related to the statement which is the conclusion.

Whether an argument is valid does not depend on whether the statements which make it up are themselves true. We do not need to conduct experiments or make some investigation of the world in order to test if an argument is valid. You will be familiar with something similar in simple arithmetic. For example:

If butter is 10p a lb, then 2 lb will cost 20p (10p $\times$ 2 = 20p)

Here, the arithmetic is correct, even though butter does not cost 10p a pound. We distinguish the question of whether the arithmetic is correct from the questions whether it is true that butter costs 10p a pound. In testing whether the arithmetic is correct, the actual price is irrelevant.

A similar distinction is made in connection with arguments. An argument may be criticised on two grounds.

1 The argument is invalid. (That is, the premises do not imply the conclusion, or, the conclusion does not follow from the premises.)
2 The premises are not true. (That is, some or all of the premises are false.)

An argument may be valid, even though the premises are false. This is similar to our arithmetical example, where the arithmetic is correct, although the information on which the calculation is based is false. It may also be the case that an argument is invalid although the premises are true. Or an argument may be such that the premises are false *and* it is invalid. If we are to be assured of the truth of the conclusion, we need to be assured of two things: that the premises are true *and* that the argument is valid. The logician is not concerned with the question of whether the premisses are in fact true, but with that of whether the premisses imply the conclusion.

Let us look again at the argument with which we began, and which we said was valid. We set it out below, with the premisses numbered:

P¹ If you are going to Spain, then you will need a passport
P² You are going to Spain
Conclusion: You will need a passport

In an argument the statement(s) which are the premisses provide reasons for the conclusion. In a valid argument the premisses do not just provide reasons, but they provide *conclusive* reasons. In this argument the premisses *do* provide conclusive reasons for the conclusion, and so it is valid.

But, you will want to know, when *do* premisses provide conclusive reasons for the conclusion? Well, suppose that the premisses of this argument are true. (Please note that we are not asking you to agree that they are true, for indeed you may know that P² at least, is false. We ask you to suppose that they are true, in the way in which you supposed that butter was 10p a pound for the sake of doing the sum.) Now, *if* the premisses are true, must the conclusion be true also, or might it be either true or false? Our argument is such that *if* the premisses are true, then the conclusion must be true. The premisses provide conclusive reasons for that conclusion. The premisses could not be true and the conclusion false. The argument is valid.

Compare this argument with the second one we gave:

P¹ If you are going to Spain, then you will need a passport
P² But you are not going to Spain
Conclusion: You will not need a passport

If these premisses are true, must the conclusion be true also, or might it be either true or false? You can see that in this case, the premises could be true and the conclusion false. (You might, after all, be going to some other country where passports are required.) Accordingly, this argument is *not* valid. The conclusion does not follow from the premises. The premises do not imply, or to be strictly accurate, do not *logically imply*, the conclusion. Of course, the statement 'You do not need a passport' taken by itself may be true. That, however, is not the point at issue. The statement which is the conclusion of the first argument may, as a matter of fact, be false, but that is not our concern. It is not part of our business to find out whether statements taken by themselves are true or false. In logic we are concerned with the relations between statements.

The validity of an argument, then, does not depend on whether the statements which make it up are themselves, as a matter of fact, true or false. We do not need to find out whether or not they are true, in order to decide whether, *if* they are true some other statement must also be true. Nor does it depend on its subject matter. Our valid argument is not valid because it is about going to Spain and needing passports, any more than our sum in simple arithmetic is correct because it is about butter. The following argument is also valid:

> If Lincoln was a Roman Emperor, then he was President of the USA
> Lincoln was a Roman Emperor
> Therefore, Lincoln was President of the USA

(Notice, by the way, that we have here an example in which the premises are as a matter of fact false, and the conclusion is as a matter of fact true. Nevertheless, it is an argument in which, *if* the premises were true the conclusion must also be true. There is no possibility that the premises be true and the conclusion false.)

If you compare our two valid arguments, you will see that they have exactly the same pattern, the same form, the same logical structure. The pattern in both cases is as follows:

> If the first, then the second
> And the first
> Therefore the second

In argument 1, the first statement which occurs is 'You are going to Spain' and the second is 'You will need a passport'. In argument 2, the first statement which occurs is 'Lincoln was a Roman Emperor' and the second statement is 'Lincoln was president of the USA'. While the statements which make up the arguments differ, the pattern, the logical structure is the same.

Instead of writing 'the first', and 'the second', it is customary in logic to use the lower case letters p, q, r ... in place of those elements of arguments which vary. We write p for the first proposition which occurs, q for the second, r for the third, if there is a third, and so on. Using these letters, which are known as *propositional variables*, the pattern which both these arguments have is:

> If p then q
> and p
> Therefore q.

Any argument having this logical structure will be valid, no matter what statements are substituted for 'p' and for 'q'. Any argument having this structure is such that if the premisses are true the conclusion must be true. Such an argument could not have true premisses and a false conclusion. If for 'p' we substitute 'Jones comes' and for 'q' we substitute 'Smith comes', we shall have the valid argument:

> If Jones comes, then Smith comes
> and Jones comes
> Therefore Smith comes

By contrast, the invalid argument has a different structure. Using 'p' for 'you are going to Spain' and 'q' for 'you will need a passport' the pattern of this argument is:

> If p then q
> and not-p
> Therefore not-q.

Any argument having this form will also be invalid, no matter what its subject matter, and no matter whether the statements which actually occur in it are as a matter of fact true, or as a matter of fact false. The *content* of the statements which make up an argument is quite irrelevant to its validity or invalidity. What matters is the way in which the statements are connected.

We have already introduced some of the symbols we shall use, and these are not very difficult to understand. Whenever we use the letters *p*, *q*, *r* . . . we shall be saying something about any proposition or propositions whatsoever. They are not themselves propositions, but are place holders for propositions. In the sections which follow we shall be introducing more symbols and we shall be explaining techniques used for testing the validity of arguments. You may think that this is unnecessary, for we have used simple arguments which most people can just *see* to be valid. Indeed, we have relied so far on your ability to see that the arguments we have presented so far are valid. It is not, however, sufficient to be able to see that an argument is valid; it is also necessary to understand *why* it is valid, and to be able to *prove* that it is.

Moreover, not all the arguments you will meet will be as simple as these, although we shall keep to simple ones to begin with. The point of using a technical procedure is that we can use it on any argument, not just on simple ones. The method of testing the validity of simple arguments is an essential part of testing the validity of more complex arguments. First, however, you must learn the techniques which involves learning the symbolic language and learning to use it. And this will take time and practice. When you turn to the following sections, read them carefully, and try to understand them, rather than trying to commit parts of it to memory. Above all, it is important that you do the exercises. If you find them difficult, then read the relevant section again. If you find them easy, do them just the same, for by doing so, you will gain facility in handling the symbolic language.

Before you turn to the next chapter, here are some questions to which you should now know the answers. If you find that you do not, please read the section again.

Exercises

1 Pick out the conclusions of the following arguments:

  (i) It will rain soon because the barometer is falling rapidly and if the barometer falls rapidly, it always rains soon.

  (ii) If the cost of living rises or government revenues increase, then the wages policy will be relaxed. But the wages policy is not going to be relaxed. Therefore, government revenues will not increase.

  (iii) Government revenues will not be increased, because the wages policy will be relaxed only if government revenues increase or the cost of living rises. And the cost of living is not going to rise.

  (iv) If the chief witness was telling the truth, then A is guilty. Moreover, the evidence was forged. So the chief witness was not telling the truth, because, if either the evidence was forged or the police were bribed, then A is not guilty.

2 (i) Are statements or arguments valid?

  (ii) Are statements or arguments true?

3 Which of the following are correct?

  (i) A valid argument may have false premisses.

  (ii) An invalid argument may have false premisses.

  (iii) A valid argument may have a false conclusion.

  (iv) An invalid argument may have a true conclusion.

  (v) An argument is valid if its premisses are true.

  (vi) An argument is valid if its conclusion is true.

  (vii) A valid argument must have true premisses.

  (viii) A valid argument is one in which, if the premisses are true the conclusion must be true.

  (ix) A valid argument cannot have true premisses and a false conclusion.

  (x) A valid argument must have a true conclusion.

  (xi) Whenever we use the letter p, we use it in place of the proposition 'You need a passport'.

  (xii) Whenever we use the letter p we use it in place of any proposition whatsoever.

4 Using the two statements: The evidence is forged. The accused is guilty – construct an argument having the form:

> If p then q
> and p
> Therefore q.

5 Which of the arguments in 1.(i)–(iv), has the form

> If p then q
> and p
> Therefore q.

2   Logical Constants (1)

Logical constants are those elements in an argument which provide its structure or form. So far, by way of examples, we have given several valid arguments, all of which have the same form. In each of these arguments, the elements which vary from one argument to another are the *statements* which make up the arguments. We introduced the letters *p*, *q*, *r* . . . to represent these. Now we must turn to the logical constants, and we shall concentrate first of all, on those which occur in the arguments we have used so far.

Now it must not be supposed that there is but one valid argument form. We have chosen to use one, for the purpose of illustration, but there are an indefinitely large number of others. Logical constants, however, are few in number. We shall use only five here, three of which we have already met. These five will yield a tremendous number of valid argument forms. They are:

Constant	Usual expression in English
negation	not . . .
material implication	if . . . then . . .
conjunction	. . . and . . .

disjunction   . . . or . . .
material equivalence   . . . if and only if . . .

These logical constants serve to make statements from other statements.

Statements are either *simple* or they are *compound*. A compound statement is one which is formed by means of a logical constant either from simple statements, or from other compound statements. The first premiss of the arguments on p. 1:

If you are going to Spain then you will need a passport

is a compound proposition which is formed by means of the logical constant 'if . . . then . . .' from the two simple propositions:

> You are going to Spain
> You will need a passport

The following are also simple propositions:

> Smith is over eighteen
> Smith is entitled to vote
> It rains
> The grass is wet

The following are compound propositions:

> *If* Smith is over eighteen, *then* he is entitled to vote
> *If* it rains, *then* the grass is wet
> The book is long *and* (the book) is boring
> Smith is *not* over eighteen

Each of the compound propositions we have given above, is formed by means of a logical constant from simple propositions. Each of these compound propositions has simple ones as components. But as we shall see when we go on to more difficult examples, some compound propositions contain as their components other compound propositions which in turn contain simple propositions as their components. A compound proposition is one that has other propositions (simple or complex) as components, but simple propositions do *not* have other propositions as components. The basic elements of any compound proposition, however complex, are simple propositions and the logical constants which form the compound propositions from the simple ones.

Every logical constant, with the exception of 'not . . .' (negation), is known as a *logical connective*. 'If . . . then . . .' and '. . . and . . .' are logical connectives, and so are the two which we shall consider later: '. . . if and only if . . .' and 'either . . . or . . .'. They are *connectives* because they form compound propositions from simple, or other compound propositions by connecting them. Each connective connects *two and only two* propositions. You will notice that in listing these connectives, we have left two spaces for two propositions. It is incorrect, both grammatically and logically, to write:

> If Smith is over eighteen then

Another proposition is needed to follow the word 'then', as in:

> If Smith is over eighteen then he is entitled to vote.

The same is true of conjunction.

> The book is long and boring

makes sense.

> The book is long and

does not.

No connective can connect more than two propositions. For example, the three propositions:

> It rains
> The grass is wet
> The match will be abandoned

cannot be connected by 'if . . . then . . .'. We have three propositions, but only two spaces for them. Of course, we could connect three propositions or even more, into one compound proposition, but we should need to use more than one connective. We can write:

> *If* it rains *then* the grass will be wet *and* the match will be abandoned.

Here we have used two connectives: 'if . . . then . . .' and '. . . and . . .'. By the use of 'if . . . then . . .' we have connected a simple proposition

It rains

and a compound proposition

> The grass is wet *and* the match will be abandoned,

in which we have two simple propositions connected by '. . . and . . .'. We make this clear by using brackets to show which two propositions are connected by which connective, thus:

> *If* it rains *then* (the grass is wet *and* the match is abandoned)

'Not . . .' or 'It is false that . . .' (negation) differs from the other logical constants. Although it is a constant, and an extremely important one, it is not a connective. It does not serve to connect two propositions. It has, as you can see, but one space to be filled. But it is like the other logical constants in that it serves to form compound propositions from other propositions. By negating the simple proposition:

You are going to Spain

we form the compound proposition

You are *not* going to Spain

or

It is false that you are going to Spain

The result of negating any simple proposition is a compound proposition. And of course, compound propositions can also be negated. For example, from the compound proposition

If the grass is wet *then* the match will be abandoned

we can form another compound proposition by negating it:

It is false that (*if* the grass is wet *then* the match will be abandoned.)

As long as you remember that this logical constant forms compound propositions from *one* other, whereas the others form compound propositions from *two* others, we can call them all constants or connectives indifferently.

Now for the symbols for these constants. The symbol for negation is $\sim$, which is known as the *tilde* sign. When any proposition is negated, the tilde sign is placed in front of it: $\sim p$. If the particular proposition which is negated is

You are going to Spain

we should write

$\sim$(You are going to Spain)

which we read

You are not going to Spain

or

It is false that . . .

or

It is not true that . . .

The symbol for 'If . . . then . . .' (material implication) is $\supset$ known as the *hook* or *horseshoe* sign. When any two propositions are connected by 'If . . . then . . .', the hook sign is placed between them: $p \supset q$.

Instead of writing:

If you are going to Spain then you will need a passport

we write

You are going to Spain $\supset$ you will need a passport

The symbol for '. . . and . . .' is likewise placed between the two propositions it connects. The symbol for this is '.' known as the *dot* sign.

When we wish to speak of any propositions whatsoever, as we have done, we use the letters $p, q, r, \ldots$ Thus, 'If it rains, the grass will be wet' is an instance of '$p \supset q$'. And so is 'If the barometer falls, it will rain.' But we also need a way of indicating that we are dealing not just with *any* compound proposition of the form 'if —, then . . .' but with some given proposition or propositions.

We shall make our task a good deal easier, if, instead of writing out each simple proposition in full, we use abbreviatory letters. Instead of writing:

'You are going to Spain' and 'You will need a passport'

we can write 'S' for 'you are going to Spain' and we can write 'P' for 'you will need a passport'.
The compound proposition:

If you are going to Spain then you will need a passport

will then be symbolised:

$$S \supset P$$

Perhaps, in doing the last exercises, you have already been using abbreviations to save yourself time. If you have, then you are obviously beginning to appreciate one of the uses of symbols. At the same time, however, we must strike a cautionary note. In logic, as in mathematics, we must adhere strictly to the rules. You must stick strictly to the rules that we give, and not take short cuts unless these are permitted. Even in using abbreviations there are rules to be followed. It is customary to use capital letters for such abbreviations. It is convenient to choose an initial letter, but care must be taken to choose a different letter to abbreviate a different proposition. For example:

Alfred was a king and Albert was a consort

must *not* be symbolised: A . A

If we use 'A' to abbreviate 'Alfred was a king', we cannot use the *same* letter to symbolise the *different* proposition 'Albert was a consort'. For such an example, it is better to use different letters, say:

> Let 'K' stand for 'Alfred was a king'
> Let 'C' stand for 'Albert was a consort'

What we have given in the last two lines is a key to the abbreviations we are using, and it is necessary to give such a key wherever there is a possibility of confusion. By giving a key, you will be able to see clearly which capital letters you have already used, and so be in no danger, in long complex propositions or arguments, of using the same capital letters to abbreviate different propositions. Unless you give a key, no one else will be in a position to see which letter abbreviates which proposition, and you yourself may forget. The need to give a key means that not much time is saved by the use of abbreviatory letters in examples which are not complex. It will be more time saving when the examples are more complex.

However, abbreviatory letters are introduced for other, and more important, reasons than simply for saving time. By using them, we are less likely to be distracted by the subject matter. More importantly, they enable us to see clearly the logical structure of the statement. When we symbolise

> Alfred was a king and Albert was a consort

as

$$K.C$$

it is quite clear that this is an instance of the conjunction of two simple propositions. This statement has the same structure as

> Jones came and Smith came

Using 'J' for 'Jones came', and 'S' for 'Smith came' this proposition is symbolised as:

$$J.S$$

This too is an instance of a conjunction of two simple propositions. Both of these examples are instances of the statement form: $p \cdot q$.

You should note the very important difference between what we have called 'abbreviatory letters' and the letters p, q, r, ... which stand for *any statements whatever*. The purpose of using the former is to highlight the logically important features of a particular proposition, simple or compound. By representing 'Alfred is a king and Albert is a consort' as 'K . C' we do three things. (i) We introduce a useful shorthand; (ii) we draw attention to the fact that the statement that we are considering is a *conjunction* of two simple propositions; (iii) we enable ourselves to ignore the subject matter of the compound proposition. (And this is especially important since the subject matter of arguments is irrelevant to their validity or invalidity.)

When we use p, q, r, ... to stand for any propositions whatever, we have all these advantages *plus* the ability to express general logical truths. For example, if we look back to our original example of a valid argument:

> If you are going to Spain, you will need a passport
> You are going to Spain
> *Therefore:* You will need a passport

we can put this into our symbolism as:

$$S \supset P \text{ and } S: \text{ therefore } P$$

(writing 'S' for 'You are going to Spain' and 'P' for 'You will need a passport').

But if we now write:

$$(p \supset q) \text{ and } p, \text{ therefore } q$$

we have a logical expression which is the form of an argument which is always valid, whatever propositions we use to replace 'p' and 'q'.

The discovery and expression of general rules is an essential part of any scientific enterprise and we could not do this in logic without the use of these so-called statement variables (or propositional variables).

The following exercises are intended for three main purposes. First, they will help you to see how compound statements are formed. Secondly, they will give you practice in using abbreviatory letters and the symbols for the logical constants. And finally, they will give you practice in recognising when two statements have the same logical form.

Exercises

Here is a list of compound statements.

(i)   If the sun shines, then the corn ripens. (S,C)
(ii)   The day is bright and sunny. (B,S)
(iii) He bought a record but he did not buy a book. (Note: Treat *but* as *and*.) (R,B)
(iv)   If he has enough money, then he will buy a book and a record.
(v)   If the car does not start, then we shall go by train.
(vi)   Jones did not come and the meeting was postponed. (J,M)
(vii) If inflation continues, then the standard of living will not rise. (I,S)
(viii) If it does not rain, then the grass will not be wet and the match will not be abandoned.
(ix)   It is false that it is wet and stormy.
(x)   If Jones comes, then Smith will come and Robinson will stay away.
(xi)   If the play is good and the acting is competent, then the author will make money.
(xii) If the play is not good then the run will be a short one. (P,R)
(xiii) If the play is good, then the run will not be a short one.
(xiv) It is false that the play will be good and the run will be short.
(xv)   The summer was not wet and the harvest was good. (S,H)
(xvi) If atomic power can be widely applied in industry, then coal mining will lose its importance. (A,C)
(xvii) If England lose the Test Match, then the team will be changed. (E,T)
(xviii) If the team is not changed, then England will lose the Test Match. (T,E)

(xix) If public spending is increased, then inflation will accelerate and taxes will not be cut.
(xx) If Smith comes, then Jones will come and Robinson will not come.

1 In which of the above propositions does 'if . . . then . . .' connect
  (a) two simple propositions? What are they?
  (b) one simple and one compound proposition? What are they?
  (c) one compound and one simple proposition? What are they?
  (d) two compound propositions? What are they?
2 (ii), (iii), (vi) and (xv) are conjunctions.
  (a) In which are two simple propositions conjoined? What are they?
  (b) In which is a simple proposition conjoined to a compound proposition? What are they?
  (c) In which is a compound proposition conjoined to a simple proposition? What are they?
3 (a) What propositions are negated in (v), (vii), (ix), (xii), (xiv) and (xx)?
  (b) Are the negated propositions simple or compound?
4 Symbolise statements (i), (ii), (iii), (v), (vi), (vii), (xii), (xiii), (xv), (xvi), (xvii), (xviii).
5 From the propositions that you have symbolised, pick out those which have the same form.

3   Logical Constants (2)

The logical connectives are called 'truth-functional'. This means that the truth or falsity of any compound statements formed by means of them can be determined solely from the truth or falsity of their component parts.

Now it may strike you as odd, after all we have said, that in logic we should be concerned with truth at all. But although we are not concerned with *factual* truth, we are concerned with truth of a very different kind. We are concerned with *logical* truth, and with *logical* falsity. To find out whether a statement is as a matter of fact true, or is as a matter of fact false, one must observe or investigate the world in some way or other. To see whether it is true that it is raining or there is cheese in the pantry, we have to look out of the window or go to the pantry. 'It is raining' and 'there is cheese in the pantry' are statements of fact and their truth or falsity depends on the state of the world. But logical truths are true, no matter what the state of the world is. A logical truth is one which is true solely by virtue of its logical structure. There are very many logical truths, and they may be very complex. We shall use simple examples.

We shall begin with logical falsity. The following are examples of logically false statements:

> The book is long and it is not long
> It is red and it is not red

Logically false statements are contradictions. We are all familiar, in ordinary conversation, with the notion of contradiction. Suppose someone is telling us about a party he went to and begins by telling us who was there: Jones was there and Smith was there. But later in his account, he says 'Jones was not there'. He has contradicted himself. A politician who said at the beginning of his speech that the cost of living was rising, but who later in the same speech denied that the cost of living was rising, would contradict himself. The statements 'The cost of living is rising' and 'The cost of living is not rising', when made in the same context are contradictory. We do not have to go outside the context of a speech to detect a contradiction. We do not have to find out exactly who was at the party before we can say that someone who asserts both 'Jones was there' and 'Jones was not there' contradicts himself. Whether it is true as a matter of fact that Jones was there, or false as a matter of fact that Jones was there, it *cannot* be true *both* that he was there and that he was not there. A logically false statement (a contradiction) is false solely because of its structure. As you can see from our examples, each consists of the conjunction of a statement and its negation. They have the form: $p . \sim p$. Any statement, regardless of its subject matter, which has the form $p . \sim p$ is a contradiction, or logically false.

The following are examples of logical truths:

> If it rains, then it rains
> If the book is red, then it is red

You will be able to see that these are true, no matter what the state of the world is. The first is true, no matter what the state of the weather, and the second is true, no matter what the colour of the book. Each of these has the same form: If p then p, or using our symbolism: $p \supset p$. Any statements which have this form are logical truths, no matter what the subject matter. The following logical truths:

If Smith was there, then he was there.
If John is over eighteen, then he is over eighteen.

have the same form. They are both instances of $p \supset p$.
There are logical truths which have different forms, as we
shall see. For now, we shall concentrate on those which have
the form: $p \supset p$

The first part of a material implication (an 'if . . . then . . .'
statement), is known as the *antecedent*, and the second part
(that which follows the hook sign), is known as the *consequent*. It is tempting to suppose that these are logical truths
because the statement which is the antecedent is the same
as that which is the consequent. They both 'say the same
thing'. But this can be misleading, and can direct our attention to the content of the statements, and this, as we have
seen, is not our concern. Each of the above statements is
such that a contradiction results if it is negated. As we shall
see later, expressions of the form:

$$\sim(p \supset p)$$

can be shown to be contradictory.

Statements which are logically true are known as *tautolo-
gies*. We have taken one simple example of a tautology
here but they can be of many different forms as we shall
see. But it is a characteristic of all of them that, if they are
negated, they yield a contradiction.

Compare these logical truths with the following:

If it rains, the match will be abandoned
If Jones comes, then Smith comes

Are these statements logically true? That is to say, do they
result in a contradiction if they are negated? The answer is
that they are not. They are neither logically true nor are they
contradictory, that is, logically false. They are known as *contingent* statements. Their truth or falsity depends upon (or is
contingent upon) the state of the world and not just on the
form of the proposition that expresses them. Again, you must
remember that though we have chosen examples which are

such that you can 'just see' that they are either logical truths or contingent statements, only a few statements are such that you can tell at a glance which they are.

We have seen that:

> If it rains, then it rains

is a logical truth. Its negation,

> It is false that if it rains, then it rains

is a statement which has the form:

$$\sim(p \supset p)$$

and is contradictory. But if a contingent statement is negated, the result will not be a contradictory statement.

> If it rains, then the match will be abandoned

is a contingent statement. Its form is:

$$(p \supset q)$$

and its negation:

> It is false that if it rains the match will be abandoned

is not a contradiction but rather another contingent statement with the form:

$$\sim(p \supset q)$$

If logical truths are negated, they yield contradictions; and conversely, if contradictions are negated, they yield logical truths. But if we negate a contingent statement we get another contingent statement.

Now although there is no connection between *factual* truth and validity, there is a very close connection between *logical* truth and validity. If a valid argument is written as a compound statement, that compound statement will be a logical truth. Let us take a simple example, by way of illustration:

> This book is long and boring
> Therefore: it is long

If we write this as a material implication, we have an instance of a logical truth:

If this book is long and boring, then it is long.

This compound statement has the form:

$$(L . B) \supset L$$

If we negate it, we should be affirming a contradiction. As we shall see later,

$$\sim[(L . B) \supset L]$$

is logically equivalent to:

$$(L . B) . \sim L$$

and this is clearly contradictory.

These matters will become clearer later when we look at a method for testing a statement to see whether it is logically true, contingent or contradictory.

The symbols for the logical constants are defined in a special way: they are defined in terms of *truth values*. Using these definitions, we can determine the truth value of any propositions, however complex they may be, formed by means of the constants, from the truth values of their component parts. Notice that we say that the symbols for the logical constants are defined in this way. This is because, although we can all use 'if . . . then . . .', '. . . and . . .' and 'not . . .' well enough in ordinary language, in logic we work with precise definitions. Moreover, the way in which some of these terms are used in logic differs, in some respects, from the ways in which they are used in ordinary language.

The term 'truth value' sounds more mysterious than it really is. On p. 4 we said that every proposition is either true or it is false. This is all that is meant by saying that every proposition has a truth value. Please note that to say that every proposition has a truth value is *not* the same as saying that every proposition is true. It would be patently absurd to say that. But every proposition is *either* true *or* it is false, that is to say, it has a truth value.

First we shall consider negation, about which we have already said something in the preceding section. Negation is defined in such a way that it accords well with the way in which we ordinarily use the concept. Moreover, it is easy to see how the truth value of any statement formed by means of this constant can be determined solely from the truth value of its component parts.

Take any proposition you like, say 'The grass is green'. Since every proposition is either true or false, this proposition is either true or false. From this simple proposition, we can form a compound one by negating it:

> The grass is not green

or

> It is false that the grass is green

If 'The grass is green' is true, then the compound statement 'The grass is not green' will be false.

If 'The grass is green' is false, then the compound statement 'The grass is not green' will be true.

This is so simple that you may feel either that you must have missed something, or that we are saying what is so obvious that it hardly needs saying. You may be assured that you have not missed anything, but do not forget that each step, although simple, is essential.

However easy to understand, the definition must be presented formally, in the symbolic language. What we have said above does not apply just to the proposition 'The grass is green'. Given any proposition whatsoever, if it is true, its negation will be false, and if it is false, its negation will be true. So, we must express our definition using the letter *p*, which we use for any proposition whatsoever, and using the correct symbol for negation. We write:

p	$\sim p$
True	False
False	True

We shall find it more convenient to adopt another method of indicating truth values, instead of laboriously writing out the words 'true' and 'false'. We could use the letters 'T' and 'F' by way of abbreviations, but these letters are easily confused. So we shall adopt the convention of writing '1' for 'true', and '0' for 'false'. Using this convention, we write the definition of negation as follows:

$$
\begin{array}{cc}
p & \sim p \\
1 & 0 \\
0 & 1
\end{array}
$$

This, as you can see, represents in symbols exactly what we wrote out above. Reading along the lines, we have first, the value of $\sim p$, when p is true, and on the second line, the value of $\sim p$, when p is false. But please notice, that in giving the truth values of $\sim p$, the zero, on the first line, is placed immediately below the tilde sign, and on the second line, the one is placed immediately under it. If you were to write these symbols under p, you would be saying that when p is true, then p is false! As we shall be operating with these symbols, it is essential to be absolutely accurate, and to get into correct habits to begin with. Failure to be accurate will at best result in confusion, and very likely, the results of the operations you perform will be inaccurate.

The other constants connect two propositions, each of which is either true, or it is false. When two propositions are taken together, they may both be true, or they may both be false. But there are also two other possibilities: the first may be true and the second false, and the first may be false and the second true. When we have two propositions taken together, there are thus four possibilities to take into account. These possibilities are listed thus:

$$
\begin{array}{cc}
p & q \\
1 & 1 \\
1 & 0 \\
0 & 1 \\
0 & 0
\end{array}
$$

Notice the order in which we have written these. Reading across the lines, we have first the possibility that both are true, on the second line that where the first is true and the second false, on the third, where the first is false and the second true, and finally, where they are both false. These possibilities must always be written in the same order. It would not have mattered if we had chosen a different order, but having chosen one, we must adhere strictly to it.

We can now define the symbol for conjunction, which is the dot sign. The definition of the conjunction sign gives the rules for assigning truth values to the conjunction of any two propositions whatsoever. It is so defined that the compound proposition is true when both conjuncts are true, but false otherwise. We give the definition below as a truth-table.

p	q	$p \cdot q$
1	1	1
1	0	0
0	1	0
0	0	0

Notice again, that we have written the values of $p \cdot q$ under the dot sign, to show that these are the truth values of the compound $p \cdot q$.

The expression '$p \cdot q$' is not a statement, but is a schema for a statement. The following statements are substitution instances of $p \cdot q$.

It is raining and the grass is wet
Smith came and Jones came
The weather is warm and we shall go swimming

The definition gives the rules for assigning truth values to any compound proposition which is formed by the conjunction of two statements.

The way in which we would ordinarily regard statements such as those listed above, accords with this definition. We should regard the compound statement 'Smith came and

Jones came' as true, if both components were true. And if the first were true and the second false, or if the first were false and the second true, we should regard the whole statement as false. And if both components were false, we should count the compound proposition false.

However, there are some peculiarities to notice. We are concerned with the conjunction of any two propositions whatsoever, and we determine the truth value of the compound, solely from the truth values of the component parts. Because of this, some apparently odd substitution instances are admitted. For example, if for '*p*', we substitute 'Smith came', and for '*q*' 'The cost of living has risen' and conjoin them, we have the compound proposition

Smith came and the cost of living has risen

According to our definition, this statement is true if both conjuncts are true, but false otherwise. Such a statement, you may feel, does not 'make sense'. It is certainly not the kind of statement we should ever be likely to make, but it is an admissible substitution instance. Another apparently odd substitution instance allowed is 'She died and fell ill'. This would not count as making sense in ordinary language, for there the temporal order matters. After all, she died after she fell ill and not before!

If you reflect for a moment, you will realise that these seem odd because we are paying attention to the subject matter of the statements. In logic, however, we are not concerned with the subject matter of statements. A consequence of defining the logical constants in terms of truth values, is that our logical system admits as substitution instances all sorts of statements that we would not ordinarily make. But, as our system will accommodate the kinds we *do* make, it does not matter if it will allow more than this.

The symbol for 'If . . . then . . .' is the hook sign ⊃. This is the sign for material implication. It, like the dot sign, is placed between the two propositions it connects. The first, that which appears before the hook sign, is known as the *antecedent*, and the second, that which follows the hook sign, is known as the *consequent*. Any compound proposition formed by means of this connective is *false* when the antecedent is true and the consequent false. Otherwise, it is true. Below, we give the definition of the hook sign.

p	q	$p \supset q$
1	1	1
1	0	0
0	1	1
0	0	1

The following are substitution instances of $p \supset q$.

If it rains then the grass is wet
If blue litmus paper is placed in acid, then it will turn red
If Jones comes then Smith comes

Again, some statements which we would not ordinarily make are admitted as substitution instances. 'If Jones comes then glass is brittle' is a substitution instance of '$p \supset q$', although it is not one we should be likely to make in intelligent conversation. Again, this does not matter, as long as we can admit the statements we would ordinarily make.

Nevertheless, it may seem odd that a statement such as 'If Jones comes then glass is brittle' is counted as an implication. Unless the first is true and the second false, the statement 'Jones comes' materially implies the statement 'glass is brittle'. In ordinary English, we usually restrict the use of the 'If . . . then . . .' relation to instances where there is some other connection. For example, we use it where there is, or we suppose that there is, some kind of connection between one fact and another, or where there is supposed to be some causal connection, as in 'If you smoke then you will get lung cancer'. We are not concerned, however, with content but with truth values.

Another peculiarity of our definition is that, not only does one statement materially imply another if both are true, regardless of content, but that one statement implies another if both are false. Thus, the compound proposition 'If Jones comes then Smith comes' is *true* if both components are false. Because of such peculiarities, the name '*material implication*' is given to this relation, which is defined solely in terms of truth values. One statement *materially implies* another in every case except where the antecedent is true and the consequent false. The justification for defining material implication in the way that we do is that it works in enabling us to distinguish between valid and invalid arguments.

Before we go on to the next chapter, here are some exercises for you to do. For some of them you will need to use the truth tables. You do not need to memorise them immediately. You will probably find that you learn them by using them.

Exercises

1 What is the truth value of $\sim p$ when p is true?
            when p is false?

2 When p is true and q is true, what are the truth values of $p \cdot q$, $p \supset q$?

3 When p is true and q is false, what are the truth values of $p \cdot q$, $p \supset q$?

4 When p is false and q is true, what are the truth values of $p \cdot q$, $p \supset q$?

5 When p is false and q is false, what are the truth values of $p \cdot q, p \supset q$?

6 Of what statement schemes are the following substitution instances?
 (a) If he passes the exam, I will eat my hat.
 (b) If it doesn't rain, we will go for a picnic.
 (c) He is both ambitious and ruthless.
 (d) It is false that he is both ambitious and ruthless.
 (e) He is not ambitious and he is not ruthless.
 (f) The money supply is not increased and inflation will fall.
 (g) If the barometer rises, it will not rain tomorrow.

7 If the following statements are negated, is the result a logical truth, a contradiction or a contingent statement?
 (a) If he says so, then he says so.

(b) If he says so, then it is so.
(c) Meat is expensive in this country.
(d) The play was successful but, on the other hand, it was not successful.
(e) He is both ambitious and ruthless.

4 Using the Definitions

Using the definitions given in the previous chapter, it is possible to determine the truth values of compound propositions in which the constants occur, no matter how complex these propositions are. We have some way to go before you are in a position to determine the truth values of complex compound propositions. We can, though, explain how the procedure works in relatively easy instances.

As our first example, we will take the statement:

If wages rise, then inflation will increase

The first step is to abbreviate this statement, using abbreviatory letters so that we can see its structure clearly.

We shall use 'W' for 'wages rise', which is the first proposition which occurs. The second is a different proposition, so we need a different letter; we shall use 'I' for 'inflation will increase'.

We write the abbreviated proposition: W ⊃ I

We can see clearly that this consists of two simple propositions connected by the hook sign.

We consult the definition of the hook sign, which tells us that any compound proposition which consists of two propositions connected by means of it, is true in every case except where the first is true and the second is false. As this is an instance of such a proposition, this will be true in every case except where the antecedent (W in this case) is true and the consequent (in this case I) is false. The truth values of W ⊃ I are exactly the same as that given in the definition of the hook sign.

Now let us consider the slightly more complex statement:

> If wages rise, then inflation will not increase

Here we have a simple statement 'wages rise' connected by 'if . . . then . . .' to a compound statement. The compound statement is the negation of 'inflation will increase'. Using the same abbreviatory letters as before, we symbolise this:

$$W \supset \sim I$$

We do not have a table from which we can read off the truth value of this statement form, as we did with the previous one. We can, however, construct one, using the definition of the hook sign and that for negation. To do this, we first write out the formula again, and underneath we list the possible ways in which two propositions can be combined:

$$
\begin{array}{cc}
W \supset \sim I \\
1 & 1 \\
1 & 0 \\
0 & 1 \\
0 & 0
\end{array}
$$

As you see, under 'W' we write the column as it appears under 'p', and under 'I' we write the column as it appears under 'q'. When any two propositions are combined, there are four possibilities: both may be true, the first true and the second false, and so on. This is what we have written under these two abbreviated statements.

Next, we refer to the definition of negation. This tells us that, if a statement is true, its negation is false, and if a statement is false, its negation is true. We fill in the column under the negation sign, writing a zero where a one appears under 'I', and a one where a zero appears, thus:

$$
\begin{array}{ccc}
\text{W} & \supset & \sim\text{I} \\
1 & & 0\ 1 \\
1 & & 1\ 0 \\
0 & & 0\ 1 \\
0 & & 1\ 0 \\
\end{array}
$$

We must do this before we deal with the hook sign, for the hook sign in this example connects W, the antecedent, with ~I, the consequent. Now we can consult the definition of the hook sign, although before we do so it is as well to strike out the column under 'I' lightly with a pencil, so that it is quite clear *which* truth values we are concerned with. To make your working simpler, you may find it helpful to number the columns as you complete them. (We shall do this for the first few examples.)

Working line by line, we consult the definition of the hook sign. On the first line, we have a true antecedent and a false conclusion. According to our definition, the truth value of a material implication with a true antecedent and a false conclusion is *false*; so we write a zero under the hook sign on the first line. On the second line, both antecedent and consequent are true, and according to the definition the compound is true. We write a one under the hook sign and carry on in the same way with the third and fourth lines. The completed table looks like this:

$$
\begin{array}{ccc}
\text{W} & \supset & \sim\text{I} \\
1 & 0 & 0\ 1 \\
1 & 1 & 1\ 0 \\
0 & 1 & 0\ 1 \\
0 & 1 & 1\ 0 \\
& (2) & (1) \\
\end{array}
$$

And we can write out the truth values of W ⊃ ~I in one line as 0111.

We will give you two other examples. First we will construct a truth-table to prove that the statement

If wages rise, then wages rise

is a logical truth. As before, the first step is to write the statement using abbreviatory letters. In this case, the same proposition 'Wages rise' recurs, so we symbolise this:

$$W \supset W$$

Any proposition is either true or it is false, so we write these possibilities under each occurrence of 'W'

$$\begin{array}{cc} W & \supset & W \\ 1 & & 1 \\ 0 & & 0 \end{array}$$

Now we consult the definition of the hook sign to ascertain the truth value of a material implication first, when both antecedent and consequent are true, and secondly when both are false. The compound in both cases is true:

$$\begin{array}{ccc} W & \supset & W \\ 1 & 1 & 1 \\ 0 & 1 & 0 \\ & (1) & \end{array}$$

We have shown that there is no possible way of assigning truth values so that we have a true antecedent and a false conclusion. We see, by the column of ones under the hook sign, that a statement of this form is always true, no matter what the truth value of its components. Compare this with the previous example. There we did not have a column of ones under the hook sign. There was one way of assigning truth values to the components of this compound statement, so that there is a true antecedent and a false consequent, the case where W is true and I is true. $W \supset W$ is a logical truth, but $W \supset \sim I$ is not.

For the third example, we will prove that the negation of a logical truth is a logical falsity (a contradiction). The negation of:

      If wages rise then wages rise

is

      It is false that if wages rise then wages rise

The statement which is negated is 'If wages rise then wages rise', so we need to place brackets around this statement to make quite clear that it is this whole statement which is negated. So, abbreviating the negated statement, we symbolise it thus:

$$\sim(W \supset W)$$

First, we construct the truth table for W ⊃ W. The truth value, which is true in every case, is given under the hook sign. Under the negation sign, we write the negation of the truth value of W ⊃ W, which gives us a column of zeros.

$$\sim(W \supset W)$$
$$0 \quad 1 \quad 1 \quad 1$$
$$0 \quad 0 \quad 1 \quad 0$$
$$(2) \quad \quad (1)$$

The statement: It is false that if wages rise then wages rise has been shown to be always false. Statements of this form: $\sim(p \supset p)$ will always be false whatever the truth-values of the components. They are logically false statements.

The procedure for determining the truth values of statements, however complicated, is exactly the same as that which we have given in this chapter. But before we can give you more complicated examples, there are a number of things we still have to explain, and a number of areas in which you will need some practice.

In the last example (and elsewhere) we used brackets, and trusted that you could understand how they were used. But more complicated examples will involve many more brackets, and we have to explain how they are used. The statements we have given as examples have been easy to symbolise, but we need to explain how more complex ones are to be symbolised, and you will need practice here. There are also two other symbols to be defined, that for material equivalence and that for alternation, and many compound statements involve these. And so far, no compound statement we have asked you to symbolise has had more than two simple statements as its components. But most compound statements we meet have more than two, so we need to explain how these are dealt with.

Before we go on, here are some exercises which will help you to see if you have understood this chapter.

Exercises

1   Using C for 'he is co-operative' and 'F' for 'he is friendly', write out the following in symbolic form:
    (a) He is co-operative and he is friendly.
    (b) If he is co-operative then he is friendly.
    (c) If he is friendly, then he is co-operative.
    (d) He is both friendly and co-operative.

2   Replacing 'A' by 'Alfred burnt the cakes' and replacing 'B' by 'Boadicea was Queen of the Iceni', write out the following in English:
    (a) A . B
    (b) B . A
    (c) B ⊃ A
    (d) A ⊃ B
    (e) A . ∼B
    (f) ∼(A . B)
    (g) ∼A ⊃ B

3   Which of the above propositions and abbreviations are substitution instances of *p . q*?
    Which are substitution instances of *p ⊃ q*?

4   Does A . B have the same truth value as B . A? Explain your answer.

5   What are the truth values of the following propositions? (Construct truth tables.)
    (a) She is poor but she is honest. (Treat 'but' as 'and'.)
    (b) She is not poor, but she is honest.
    (c) She is poor but she is not honest.
    (d) If she is honest, then she is not poor.
    (e) If she is not poor then she is not honest.
    (f) It is false that she is poor and she is honest.

6   Prove, by constructing a truth table, that the statement 'The book is red and not red' is logically false.

5 Using Brackets

No matter how complex a compound proposition may be, we can always ascertain its truth value by constructing a truth-table. We might, for instance, have a proposition in which two compound propositions are connected and each of these propositions may also be compound. But however complex a compound proposition may be, it can always be analysed into the simple propositions which are its components, and the logical constants which connect them.

Each of the connectives connects two and only two propositions, whether these be simple or compound. So, if we have a proposition in which two compound propositions are connected, or in which one simple proposition is connected to a compound one, it is essential to make clear *which* two propositions are connected. This we do by using brackets. For example, the proposition:

If inflation continues, then prices will rise and unemployment will increase

may be symbolised: $I \supset (P \cdot U)$. (We have used 'I' for 'Inflation continues'. 'P' for prices will rise' and 'U' for 'unemployment will increase'.) By using brackets, we have made quite clear which are the two propositions connected by the hook sign, and which are the two propositions connected by the dot sign. We shall find that in more complex propositions we need to use other brackets. If, for instance, we wanted to conjoin the above proposition to yet another, say 'inflation will continue' we should need to enclose the above proposition in brackets, thus:

$$[I \supset (P \cdot U)] \cdot I$$

By using brackets in this way, we show quite clearly that it is the whole of the expression enclosed within the square brackets which is connected by ' . ' to I. If we have an even more complex proposition, we shall need to use braces as well.

If we were to omit the brackets from the form: $I \supset (P \cdot U)$ we should have an ambiguous and, therefore, ill-formed expression. From $I \supset P \cdot U$ we cannot tell whether the hook sign connects I and P, or whether it connects I and the compound proposition $P \cdot U$. It displays the same kind of ambiguity as does the arithmetical expression $7 + 5 \times 3$. We cannot tell from this which operation to perform first. We cannot tell whether we are first to add 7 and 5 and then multiply by 3, or whether we are to add 7 to the result of multiplying 5 and 3. We know, because we learned in our schooldays, that this expression can be rendered unambiguous by the use of brackets, thus $(7 + 5) \times 3$. And we know now how to proceed, because we also learned the rules governing the use of brackets in arithmetic.

The constants ' . ' and '$\supset$' connect two and only two propositions, that which immediately precedes the connective, and that which immediately follows it, whether these are simple or compound. That is to say, the *scope* of these constants is that expression which immediately precedes it, and that which immediately follows it. Thus, in

$$\text{(i) } p \cdot (q \supset r)$$

the scope of the dot sign is p (which immediately precedes it) and the whole of the form enclosed in the round brackets. The scope of the hook sign is q and r.

Consider the form:

$$(ii)\ (p \supset q) . (r \supset s)$$

Here the scope of the first occurrence of the hook sign is *p*
and *q*, the scope of the second is *r* and *s*. The scope of the
dot sign is the compound propositions enclosed in round
brackets on either side of it.

Here is an example in which there are more brackets:

$$(iii)\ [(p \supset q) . (r \supset s)] \supset (p \supset q)$$

In this example, the whole of the expression contained
within the square brackets is connected by means of the
hook sign to that enclosed within round brackets on the
right-hand sign of the hook sign. In this material implication,
the antecedent is the whole expression contained within the
square brackets, and the consequent is the expression contained within the round brackets. The scope of the dot sign
is the two expressions enclosed in round brackets $(p \supset q)$ on
the left of it, and $(r \supset s)$ on the right. The antecedent is a
conjunction of two compound propositions.

It is important not to allow yourself to be confused by the
brackets. Look carefully at each example, to see how it is
made up. If you are at all confused, go back to the beginning
of the chapter, and examine each expression in the light of
the text

In compound propositions which have other compound
propositions as their components, *one* of the connectives is
the *main* connective. The main connective is that which has
the widest scope. It is that which ranges over the whole
expression In example (i) the dot sign is the main connective,
as it is also in example (ii). In (iii) the main connective is the
hook sign, and in the following example:

$$[(p . q) \supset r] . {\sim} r$$

the *second* occurrence of the dot sign is the main connective.
Example (i) $p . (q \supset r)$, the main connective of which is

the dot sign, is a conjunction. The two conjuncts are *p*, and (*q* ⊃ *r*).

Example (ii) (*p* ⊃ *q*) . (*r* ⊃ *s*), the main connective of which is also the dot sign, is a conjunction. The two conjuncts are (*p* ⊃ *q*), and (*r* ⊃ *s*).

Example (iii) [(*p* ⊃ *q*) . (*r* ⊃ *s*)] ⊃ (*p* ⊃ *q*), where the hook sign is the main connective, is a material implication, having [(*p* ⊃ *q*) . (*r* ⊃ *s*)] as the antecedent and (*p* ⊃ *q*) as the consequent.

The exercises which follow are designed to help you find your way about formulae which include brackets. We have used other propositional variables besides *p* and *q*, but this does not matter at all for what you are asked to do. We have also given some exercises which include rather a lot of brackets. Do not be bothered by this. Work systematically and look carefully for the different kinds of brackets.

Exercises

1 In the following propositional form:

$$(p \supset q) . (r \supset s)$$

What is the scope of each occurrence of ⊃ ?
Which is the main connective?

2 (*p* . *r*) ⊃ (*r* . *s*)
What is the scope of ⊃ ?
Which is the main connective?

3 [(*s* ⊃ *t*) . (*t* ⊃ *r*)] ⊃ (*s* ⊃ *r*)
What is the scope of the dot sign?
Which is the main connective?

4 [(*s* ⊃ *t*) . (*t* ⊃ *r*)] ⊃ [(*s* ⊃ *r*) . (*r* . *w*)]
What is the scope of the *third* occurrence of the dot sign?
Which is the main connective?

5 (*p* ⊃ *q*) . [(*w* ⊃ *r*) . (*q* ⊃ *w*)]
What is the scope of the *first* occurrence of the dot sign?
What is the main connective?

6 {[(*s* ⊃ *t*) . (*t* ⊃ *r*)] . (*p* ⊃ *q*)} . [(*p* ⊃ *q*) . (*r* ⊃ *s*)]
Which is the main connective?
What is the scope of the *second* occurrence of the dot sign?

What is the scope of the *first* occurrence of the dot sign?
7 Say which of the above formulae in 1–6 are:
   (a) conjunctions. What are the conjuncts?
   (b) material implications. What are the antecedents and
       consequents?

6 Negation

The scope of the negation sign is that expression which immediately follows it, whether this be simple or compound. Here are some examples:

1 $\sim p$, the scope of the negation sign is p.
   There is no need for brackets here, for the scope of the negation sign is a simple proposition.
2 $\sim p \supset q$
   Here again, the scope of the negation sign is p.
   The scope of the hook sign is $\sim p$ (on the left-hand side) and q on the right-hand side.
3 $\sim(p \supset q)$
   Here the scope of the negation sign is the whole of the expression within the round brackets. The form which is negated is the compound $p \supset q$.
4 $\sim[p \supset (q \cdot r)]$
   The scope of the negation sign is the whole of the expression which immediately follows it. In this example, it is the whole of the expression contained within the square brackets.
5 $p \supset \sim(q \cdot r)$
   In this example, the scope of the negation sign is $(q \cdot r)$.

The negation sign is the *main* constant when its scope is the whole expression. In examples 3 and 4 it is the main constant. In 1, of course, it is the *only* constant. In examples 2 and 5 it is not the main constant. In both of these examples, the main constant is the hook sign. In 2, the hook sign connects ~p, and q; in 5, the hook sign connects p, and ~(q . r)

Now do the following exercises:

Exercises

(*A*) What is the scope of the negation sign(s) in the following?

1   ~p ⊃ q
2   ~(p . q)
3   p ⊃ ~q
4   ~(p . q) ⊃ (r ⊃ s)
5   ~[(p . q) ⊃ (r . s)]
6   ~[~(r . s) . (t ⊃ u)]
7   ~p . ~q
8   ~(r ⊃ s) ⊃ ~(t . u)
9   ~(r ⊃ s) ⊃ (~t . u)

(*B*) Which is the main constant in each of the above examples?

7 Determining the Truth Values of Complex Propositions

Our next task is to explain how we determine the truth value of a compound proposition in which brackets are used. Let us take as our first example, any proposition having the form:

$$(p \supset q) \cdot (q \supset p)$$

Two variables occur in this example, so we shall need four lines. First, we assign truth values to these variables. In case you have forgotten, we give again the standard way in which truth values are assigned to two propositions taken together,

$$
\begin{array}{cc}
p & q \\
1 & 1 \\
1 & 0 \\
0 & 1 \\
0 & 0 \\
\end{array}
$$

Under the first occurrence of p in our formula, we write the column which appears under p; under q in our formula, we write the column which appears under q. When q recurs, we write again the column for q, and when p recurs we write the column for p.

$$(p \supset q) \cdot (q \supset p)$$

1	1	1	1
1	0	0	1
0	1	1	0
0	0	0	0

Now we need to know where to begin. We begin with that constant which has the *least* scope. To find out which this is, we look first for the main connective, which in this case is the dot sign. We have here a conjunction, the conjuncts of which are both compound propositions. We have a truth table for conjunction, which will give us the truth value of any two propositions connected by the dot sign, given the truth values of those propositions. Before we can use that, we have to ascertain the truth values of each of these conjuncts.

The compound proposition on the left-hand side consists of two simple propositions connected by the hook sign, and we have the truth values for the simple propositions, so we begin here. We consult the definition of the hook sign, and fill in the column under the hook sign in our example, just as we did in the examples on p. 35.

The compound proposition on the right-hand side of the conjunction, also consists of two simple propositions connected by means of the hook sign, so we can assign truth values to this proposition. (Remember that we concern ourselves *solely* with truth values.) On the first line, we have the hook sign connecting two propositions, both of which have the truth value *true*, so we consult the definition to see what is the truth value of a material implication with true antecedent and true consequent. This is *true*, so we fill that in. On the next line, we have a false antecedent and a true consequent, which is again *true*, so we fill that in. We proceed down the column in this fashion. We now have:

$$(p \supset q) \cdot (q \supset p)$$

1	1	1		1	1	1
1	0	0		0	1	1
0	1	1		1	0	0
0	1	0		0	1	0

The columns under the hook sign give the truth values of the compound propositions $(p \supset q)$ and $(q \supset p)$. Strike out lightly the columns you have finished with. We now have the truth values of both conjuncts, so, consulting the truth table for the dot sign, we can fill in the column under that in our example. The truth value of a conjunction when both conjuncts are true (first line) is *true*; when the first is false and the second is true (second line), the compound is false. We fill in these truth values, and proceed line by line until the column is complete. We can write out the truth value on one line.

$$(p \supset q) \cdot (q \supset p)$$

$$\begin{array}{ccccccc} 1 & 1 & 1 & 1 & 1 & 1 & 1 \\ 1 & 0 & 0 & 0 & 0 & 1 & 1 \\ 0 & 1 & 1 & 0 & 1 & 0 & 0 \\ 0 & 1 & 0 & 1 & 0 & 1 & 0 \\ & (1) & & (3) & & (2) & \end{array}$$

Here is another, rather more difficult example:

$$(p \cdot \sim q) \supset \sim(p \supset q)$$

First, we assign truth values to the variables, as before

$$(p \cdot \sim q) \supset \sim(p \supset q)$$

$$\begin{array}{ccccc} 1 & 1 & & 1 & 1 \\ 1 & 0 & & 1 & 0 \\ 0 & 1 & & 0 & 1 \\ 0 & 0 & & 0 & 0 \end{array}$$

Next, we look for the main connective, which in this case is the first occurrence of the hook sign. As this connects two compound propositions, look at the left-hand one first. The main connective here is the dot sign, which connects the simple proposition p, with the compound one, $\sim q$. The negation sign is that with the least scope, so we begin here, filling in the column under the negation sign in the formula according to the definition. Now we can fill in the column under the dot sign, for we now have the truth values

on each side of it. (Strike out the column under q, for we
have finished with it.)

Now we have:

$$(p \cdot \sim q) \supset \sim(p \supset q)$$

1 0 0 1	1	1
1 1 1 0	1	0
0 0 0 1	0	1
0 0 1 0	0	0
(2)(1)		

Now we have the truth value of the antecedent, we turn to
the consequent. Here the main connective is the negation
sign, for its scope is the whole of the expression within the
round brackets. Obviously, until we have the truth of the
expression within the round brackets, we cannot negate it. We
begin with the expression in the round brackets, filling in the
column under the hook sign according to the definition.
When we have the truth value of that expression, we can
strike out the columns we no longer need. Next we fill
in the column under the negation sign, writing false where
the expression within the brackets is true, and true when
the expression within the brackets is false.

$$(p \cdot \sim q) \supset \sim(p \supset q)$$

1 0 0 1	0	1 1 1
1 1 1 0	1	1 0 0
0 0 0 1	0	0 1 1
0 0 1 0	0	1 1 0
(2)(1)		(4) (3)

Now we have the truth value of the expressions on either
side of the hook sign, which is the main connective, we can
assign a truth value to the whole expression. Written on one
line, it is 1111.

Have you noticed that this is a logical truth? That this is
so, is indicated by the column of ones. No matter what
truth values are assigned to the variables a proposition
having this form is always true. Unlike our previous example

of logical truths, this is not one of the kind which you could see at a glance.

As a last example, before you try to construct some examples for yourself, take:

$$\sim[\sim(p \supset q) \supset (\sim p \supset q)]$$

The main connective here is the first negation sign, for its scope is the whole of the expression within the square brackets. And that expression is:

$$\sim(p \supset q) \supset (\sim p \supset q)$$
$$\text{(M)}$$

The main connective here is indicated by 'M' below the hook sign. If we break up the expression to show main connectives and least scopes in its two parts, we have:

$$\sim(p \supset q) \qquad \sim p \supset q$$
$$\text{(M)} \qquad\qquad \text{(M)}$$
$$p \supset q \qquad\quad \sim p$$
least scope   least scope

Beginning at the left-hand side with that constant which has the least scope and working systematically as with the previous examples, we assign a truth value to the expression within the square brackets:

$$\sim[\sim(p \supset q) \supset (\sim p \supset q)]$$

	0	1	1	1	1		0	1	1	1
	1	1	0	0	1		0	1	1	0
	0	0	1	1	1		1	0	1	1
	0	0	1	0	1		1	0	0	0

$$(2) \quad (1) \quad\; (5) \;\; (3) \;\; (4)$$

Here we have numbered the columns in the order in which we have worked them. The truth values of the antecedent are given under the second negation sign (column labelled (2)) and those of the consequent under the third hook sign (column labelled (4)). It remains to negate the truth value of the expression within the square brackets,

given in the column numbered (5). (We leave this to you.)
This is a uniform column of ones indicating that the expression within the square brackets is a logical truth. The
result of negating this gives a column of zeros. This is the
sign of a logically contradictory expression which always
takes the value 'false' no matter what truth values are
assigned to the variables making it up. Just as expressions
with a uniform column of ones are logical truths, those
which have a column of zeros are contradictions or logically
false expressions.

Exercises

Construct truth tables for the following expressions:

1   $\sim p \supset q$
2   $\sim(p \cdot q)$
3   $p \supset \sim q$
4   $\sim p \cdot \sim q$
5   $(p \supset q) \cdot (\sim q \supset p)$
6   $(\sim p \cdot q) \supset (p \supset \sim q)$
7   $\sim(\sim p \supset q) \cdot \sim(p \supset \sim q)$
8   $\sim[(\sim p \cdot \sim q) \supset (q \supset p)]$
9   $\sim[(p \supset q) \supset (\sim q \supset \sim p)]$
10 $\sim[\sim(\sim p \cdot q) \supset (\sim q \cdot \sim p)]$

8 Expressions with Three Variables

So far we have discussed only rather simple examples of expressions involving two propositions. But many arguments involve more than two propositions and we shall have to extend the use of the truth-table method as we have used it so far to deal with these more complex cases. As a first approach to these more difficult cases, consider expressions involving three propositions. With one proposition, there are two ways of covering all the possible truth-values; the proposition is either true or false. With two propositions, as we have seen, there are four ways of listing all possible combinations of truth-values; both true, first true and second false, first false and second true and both false. When we have three propositions we can argue as follows. There are two possible truth values for the third proposition, true and false. And each of these has to be combined with the four truth-possibilities of the first two propositions, giving eight possibilities in all. They can be listed as follows:

p	q	r
1	1	1
1	1	0

p	q	r
1	0	1
1	0	0
0	1	1
0	1	0
0	0	1
0	0	0

Suppose that we have the following logical form to evaluate:

$$[(p \supset q) . (q \supset r)] \supset (p \supset r)$$

We fill in the columns of ones and zeros under the three variables as we have done above:

```
[(p ⊃ q) . (q ⊃ r)] ⊃ (p ⊃ r)
 1   1    1   1       1   1
 1   1    1   0       1   0
 1   0    0   1       1   1
 1   0    0   0       1   0
 0   1    1   1       0   1
 0   1    1   0       0   0
 0   0    0   1       0   1
 0   0    0   0       0   0
```

Once we have done this the empty columns under the logical connectives can be completed, in the usual way, starting with those of least scope and numbering the columns as we complete them. The final table looks like this:

```
[(p ⊃ q) . (q ⊃ r)] ⊃ (p ⊃ r)
 1 1  1  1 1 1  1   1   1 1  1
 1 1  1  0 1 0  0   1   1 0  0
 1 0  0  0 0 1  1   1   1 1  1
 1 0  0  0 0 1  0   1   1 0  0
 0 1  1  1 1 1  1   1   0 1  1
 0 1  1  0 1 0  0   1   0 1  0
 0 1  0  1 0 1  1   1   0 1  1
 0 1  0  1 0 1  0   1   0 1  0
   1     4  2      5    3
```

This final column (5) under the constant of widest scope

shows only ones. This, as we know, is the sign of a logically true expression.

Here are some exercises with three variables.

Exercises

Complete truth-tables for the following expressions:

1 $(p \cdot q) \supset (q \cdot r)$
2 $(\sim p \cdot q) \supset (\sim q \cdot r)$
3 $\sim(p \supset q) \supset (q \cdot r)$
4 $[(p \supset q) \supset r] \supset [(p \cdot q)] \supset r]$
5 $[(\sim p \supset \sim q) \supset r] \supset [\sim r \supset (p \cdot q)]$
6 $[(p \supset q) \cdot (q \supset r)] \supset (p \supset r)$
7 $[(\sim p \cdot q) \supset \sim r] \supset [(r \cdot \sim q) \supset \sim p]$
8 $[(p \supset r) \supset (\sim r \supset \sim p)] \supset (p \supset p)$
9 $[(p \supset r) \cdot (\sim q \supset \sim r)] \supset (\sim q \supset \sim p)$
10 $[(p \cdot r) \supset \sim q] \supset [q \supset \sim(p \cdot r)]$

9 Translating Words into Symbols

We are almost in the position of being able to test the validity of arguments of the kind we have given so far. We said earlier that an argument can be written as a compound statement. If the argument is valid, then that statement will be a logical truth. In order to test the validity of arguments, we first symbolise the argument as a compound statement form, and then use truth tables to see if it is a logical truth. We begin by explaining how arguments are to be written as compound statements, and how they are to be symbolised, using brackets, to avoid ambiguity. Let us take as an example:

> If arsenic is poisonous, then it will cure colds
> Arsenic is poisonous
> Therefore it will cure colds

This argument is written above, in standard form, with the premisses given on the first two lines, and the conclusion on the third.

In any argument, the conclusion purports to follow from the premisses. If the argument is valid, then the conclusion does follow from the premisses. That is to say, if the premisses are accepted, *then* the conclusion must be accepted, on pain of self-contradiction. So we can write out the argument as a material implication, with the premisses as the antecedent and the conclusion as the consequent. Thus:

If (premiss 1 and premiss 2) *then* conclusion

Any argument will have 'if . . . then . . .' as its main connective, so we write the premisses to the left of the hook sign, and the conclusion to the right, thus:

(If arsenic is poisonous, then it will cure colds, and arsenic is poisonous) ⊃ arsenic will cure colds

It is essential, in symbolising compound statements, to remember what was said in the section on bracketing. Each connective connects two and only two statements, and so we have used brackets to show which statements are connected by the main connective, which is the hook sign.

Next, we turn to the antecedent, and look for the main connective there. What we have here is a conjunction of a compound proposition – 'If arsenic is poisonous, then it will cure colds' and a simple proposition, 'it (arsenic) will cure colds'.

(If arsenic is poisonous, then it will cure colds) . arsenic is poisonous

We cannot, without further ado, connect the antecedent with the consequent by means of the hook sign. For if we did, there would be an ambiguity. We have to make it quite clear that it is the two statements which constitute the antecedent which are connected with the consequent, so we need to bracket the premisses together using square brackets, thus:

[(If arsenic is poisonous then it will cure colds) . (arsenic is poisonous)] ⊃ arsenic will cure colds

We have almost, but not quite, reduced our compound statement to the simple statements which are its components, and the logical connectives between them. When we have replaced 'if . . . then . . .' in the first part of the antecedent by the hook sign, we have:

[(Arsenic is poisonous ⊃ it will cure colds) . arsenic is poisonous] ⊃ arsenic will cure colds

The final step is to use abbreviatory letters for the simple propositions. Using 'A' for 'arsenic is poisonous' and 'C' for 'arsenic will cure colds' we write:

$$[(A \supset C) . A] \supset C$$

Not every argument is presented in as convenient a form as we have presented this, where the premisses are given first, and the conclusion last. Sometimes, as we pointed out on p. 3, arguments are presented in such a way that the conclusion is not given last. In the following example, the conclusion is given first:

It will rain soon, because the barometer is falling rapidly and if the barometer falls rapidly, it always rains soon

In our first example, the conclusion was signalled by means of the word 'therefore'. In this example, it is the premisses which are signalled by the word 'because'. You will need to look carefully for the conclusion. However the argument is presented, it is the conclusion which follows, or is supposed to follow, from the premisses, and so it is the conclusion which is the consequent of the material implication. The premisses are the antecedent. So, you must begin symbolising the argument given above by writing the premisses as the antecedent:

(The barometer is falling rapidly and if the barometer falls rapidly it always rains soon) ⊃ (it will rain soon)

Before we go further, it will be as well if you have some practice in symbolising compound propositions which require the use of brackets. But remember that not all compound statements are arguments. After all, the premisses of the above argument constitute a compound statement: the simple proposition 'the barometer is falling rapidly' is connected by 'and' with the compound proposition 'if the barometer falls rapidly then it always rains'. So do not expect that the main connective in each of the exercises we shall give you will be the hook sign. Remember too, that negation is a logical constant, and can also be the main constant. The procedure to be followed is the same as that which we have followed:

1 Look for the main connective.
2 Bracket the two propositions it connects.
3 Examine first the proposition which occurs on the left-hand side. Is this simple or compound?
4 If it is compound, look for the main connective.
5 Bracket the two propositions it connects, remembering to add to, or to change the first brackets, if this is necessary.
6 Repeat the procedure until the left-hand side is reduced to simple propositions and the logical connections between them.
7 Repeat the procedure with the right-hand side.
8 Replace the simple propositions with abbreviatory letters.

Exercises

Symbolise the following:

1 If Smith comes then Jones will come, and Smith will come, so Jones will come. (Use S for 'Smith will come', and J for 'Jones will come'.)
2 If the bus is late we shall miss our train; and we shall miss our train because the bus is late. (B: the bus is late; M: we shall miss our train.)
3 If Jones comes then Smith will come, and if Smith comes, then Jones will come. (As 1.)
4 He bought a record and a book. (R: he bought a record; B: he bought a book.)

5 It is false that he bought a record and a book.
6 He bought a record, but he did not buy a book.
7 It is not true that if arsenic is poisonous then it will cure colds. (A: arsenic is poisonous; C: arsenic will cure colds.)
8 If the chief witness was telling the truth then A is guilty. And A is guilty. (C: chief witness is telling the truth; G: A is guilty.)
9 If the chief witness is telling the truth, then A is guilty. But A is not guilty.
10 If the chief witness is telling the truth then A is guilty. But A is not guilty; so the chief witness is not telling the truth.
11 The rates are not due; because if they are due we get a demand and we have not had a demand. (R: rates are due; D: we have a demand.)
12 The evidence was not forged and the police were not bribed. (E: the evidence was forged; B: the police were bribed.)
13 If the evidence was forged and the police were bribed, the press will keep quiet. (P: the press will keep quiet.)
14 If the barometer doesn't rise then the weather won't improve and the match will be cancelled. (B: the barometer will rise. W: the weather will improve. M: the match will be cancelled.)
15 If she marries, she will make her husband miserable; and if she doesn't marry, she will make herself miserable. (M: she marries; H: she will make her husband miserable; S: she will make herself miserable.)

10 Testing the Validity of Arguments

We are now in a position to test the validity of arguments of the kind we have given so far. Let us take as an example the first argument we gave:

If you are going to Spain, then you will need a passport
You are going to Spain
Therefore, you will need a passport

We can now prove that this argument is valid, by writing it as a material implication, and constructing a truth-table. You have already followed the necessary procedures in the preceding sections. We list these below.

1 Write the argument as a material implication, with the premisses as the antecedent and the conclusion as the consequent.
2 Symbolise, using abbreviatory letters.
3 Count the number of simple propositions. If two, you will need four lines, one for each of the four combinations of truth values which are possible for two propositions. If three, you will need eight lines. Our example has two.

4   Assign truth values to the simple propositions. If there
    are two, write the column as given under *p* and *q*, writing
    the column for *p* under the first letter that occurs, and
    the column for *q* under the second. If there are three
    letters, you will need to refer to the table for *p, q, r*, again,
    writing the column for *p* under the first letter that occurs,
    the column given under *q* for the second, and that given
    under *r* for the third.
5   Assign truth values to the statement form, following the
    procedure given in section 7.
6   If the completed truth-table has a column of one under
    the main connective, then the statement form is a logical
    truth. It would then have been shown that there is no
    possibility of assigning truth values in such a way that
    there is a true antecedent and a false conclusion. The
    argument which has been written as a material implica-
    tion, with the premisses as the antecedent and the con-
    clusion as the consequent has been shown in this way to
    be valid. For it would have been shown that an argument
    of this form can never have true premisses and a false
    conclusion. The premisses logically imply the conclusion.
7   If the completed truth-table does not have a column of
    ones under the main connective, then the statement is
    not a logical truth. The argument which was written as a
    material implication is *not* valid. There is the possibility
    of its having true premisses and a false conclusion.

Written as a material implication, our argument is:

If (if you are going to Spain you will need a passport
and you are going to Spain) then you will need a passport

Using S for 'You are going to Spain' and P for 'you will
need a passport', it is symbolised:

$$[(S \supset P) . S] \supset P$$

Below we have assigned truth values to the propositions:

$$[(S \supset P) . S] \supset P$$

1	1	1	1
1	0	1	0
0	1	0	1
0	0	0	0

Below we have assigned a truth value to the whole compound proposition, according to the procedure given in section 7. We have numbered the steps in the order in which we have taken them:

```
([S ⊃ P) . S] ⊃ P
1 1 1   1 1 1 1
1 0 0   0 1 1 0
0 1 1   0 0 1 1
0 1 0   0 0 1 0
 (1)    (2) (3)    Valid
```

The result, as you see, is a column of ones under the main column, so we have shown that it is valid.

The completed truth-table for the second argument we gave:

If you are going to Spain, you will need a passport
But you are not going to Spain
Therefore you will not need a passport

looks like this:

```
[(S ⊃ P) . ~S] ⊃ ~P
1 1 1  0 0 1 1  0 1
1 0 0  0 0 1 1  1 0
0 1 1  1 1 0 0  0 1
0 1 0  1 1 0 1  1 0
 (1)   (3)(2) (5)(4)   Invalid
```

As you see, we do not have a complete column of ones under the main connective, so the material implication is not a logical truth, and the argument which was written as this material implication is not valid.

If you have understood the preceding sections, you will

have no difficulty in testing the validity of some arguments, and you will be able to do the following exercises. If you find that you have difficulty, then return to sections 7–10, and work over them again. Once you have mastered them, you have a means of testing the validity of any arguments whatsoever which depend on the logical constants 'if . . . then . . .', '. . . and . . .' and 'not'. When we have explained the remaining two constants, you will have a means of testing the validity of a great variety of arguments at this level of logic.

Exercises

Use truth-tables to test the validity of the following arguments: (Remember to indicate whether the argument is valid or invalid.)

1   If Churchill was English, then Kennedy was Greek.
    Churchill was English,
    Therefore: Kennedy was Greek.
2   If wishes are horses, then beggars ride.
    But wishes are not horses.
    Therefore: beggars do not ride.
3   If wishes are horses, then beggars ride.
    But beggars do not ride.
    Therefore: wishes are not horses.
4   If Lincoln was a Roman Emperor, then he was President of the USA.
    Lincoln was President of the USA.
    Therefore: Lincoln was a Roman Emperor.
5   The book is long and boring.
    Therefore: the book is long.
6   The book is long.
    Therefore: the book is long and boring.
7   If the chief witness is telling the truth, then A is guilty. But A is not guilty, and *so* the chief witness is not telling the truth.
8   If the doctor prescribes antibiotics, the infection will be halted.
    If the infection is halted, the patient's temperature will fall.
    Therefore: if the doctor prescribes antibiotics, the patient's temperature will fall.

9 If the infection is halted, the patient's temperature will fall. *So*, if the patient's temperature does not fall, the infection will not be halted.

10 If the doctor prescribes antibiotics, the infection will be halted.
   If the infection is halted, the patient's temperature will fall.
   The doctor prescribes antibiotics.
   Therefore: the patient's temperature will fall.

11 If the Aztecs practised human sacrifice, then their civilisation was inferior to that of the Conquistadores. If their civilisation was inferior to that of the Conquistadores, then it was fortunate that the Aztecs were defeated. *Therefore:* if it was not fortunate that the Aztecs were defeated, they did not practise human sacrifice.

12 If the evidence was forged and the police were bribed, then A is not guilty. *Therefore:* if A is guilty, it is false that the evidence was forged and the police were bribed.

13 If the evidence was forged, then the police were bribed. If the police were bribed, then it is possible that the journalists were telling the truth. But it is not possible that the journalists were telling the truth.
   Therefore: the evidence was not forged.

14 If the picture is not a forgery, then it is valuable. If the picture is not by Vermeer, then it is not valuable. *Therefore:* if the picture is not by Vermeer, it is a forgery.

15 If exports increase, then the labour situation will improve and the government will survive. The government will not survive. *So* exports will not increase.

11 Translating into Logical Symbolism

So far, all the examples we have used have been quite straightforward. The statements and arguments that we have asked you to translate into symbols have been chosen so that you would have little difficulty in recognising their logical form. This will not always be so, either within this book, or in the statements and arguments you will meet outside it.

Once we have the logical form of a statement, we can ascertain its truth value in a mechanical manner, using the truth tables for the definitions of the logical constants. But extracting the logical form of a statement is *not* a mechanical procedure. In translating words into symbols, great care must be taken to render accurately the logical form. This will require thought and attention to the sense of the statements and arguments. We cannot, for example, automatically treat every statement in which the word 'and' occurs as a conjunction, and translate the word 'and' into the dot sign. The dot sign is the sign for conjunction, and only those instances where the word 'and' conjoins two statements can correctly be translated into the dot sign. The word 'and' does not always do the work of a conjunction. The following statement *is* an example in which 'and' does the work of conjunction:

John and Mary are here

This has the logical sense of:

John is here and Mary is here

and so is symbolised:

J . M

But now consider:

John and Mary are married

Here, the word 'and' *may* work as a conjunction. If for instance, this were said in answer to the question 'How are your children?', then 'and' would work as a conjunction. The statement would be correctly rendered as a conjunction of the two simple statements: John is married, and Mary is married. We should be able to tell from the context if the statement is to be understood in this way.

But more often, what is meant by such a statement is that John and Mary are married to *each other*. The sense of this statement is not *fully* rendered by treating this as the conjunction of the two statements: John is married, and Mary is married. In this case, we are asserting that a certain relation holds between John and Mary. Such a statement is a relational one, and is outside the scope of the propositional calculus. To deal with such statements, we need more logical apparatus than we shall be able to use in the course of this book.

So do, please, remember when you are asked to symbolise statements, that it is not an automatic procedure, and that you may have to look carefully for the logical form. Remember that the dot sign is the sign for conjunction and only those words which do the work of conjunctions should be be translated into it. There are other such words besides 'and'; 'but' is one we have already used. Others are 'although', 'moreover', 'still' and 'yet'. Examples are:

> Smith went to London but Jones stayed home
> Smith went to London although Jones went too

Care must also be taken with negation. We have already given some locutions for this:

> It is false that . . .
> It is not true that . . .
> It is not the case that . . .

But negation is also signified in English by the use of prefixes. 'Imprecise' means 'not precise', and should be symbolised accordingly. 'Unpunctual' and 'ungrateful' mean 'not punctual' and 'not grateful', and should be symbolised accordingly. 'Illegal' and 'illegible' are two others. The statement:

> His writing was legible and illegible

which is a contradiction, must be symbolised:

$$L . \sim L$$

as a conjunction of a statement and its negation. If we were to symbolise this as L . I, we should not have a contradictory form. Any statement which has the form $p . \sim p$ is a contradiction. although you may need to look carefully to see that a statement has that form.

There may be statements which you are reluctant to characterise as contradictions. You may feel that a statement like 'It is raining and it is not raining' is different from one like 'His writing was legible and illegible'. It is true that if anyone were to state the former, we should not ordinarily accuse him of self-contradiction as we would if he were to make the latter statement. If someone of whom we asked 'Is it raining?' were to say 'It is and it isn't', we should understand what the weather was like. But for all that, the statement *is* a conjunction of a statement and its negation. It is a contradiction, and must be symbolised as one. Our logical apparatus is designed to deal with any statement whatsoever, and we cannot make exceptions to allow for nuances of language arising from the context in which statements are made. To do so would violate the rule we laid down, that every statement is either true, or false, and cannot be both.

Conditional statements are not always presented in such a way that the antecedent occurs first. In the statement:

If the train is late we shall miss our connection

the antecedent is given first. The statement is symbolised: L ⊃ M.

But the very same statement might be presented in such a way that the antecedent is given last:

We shall miss our connection *if* the train is late

The logical form is exactly the same: L ⊃ M.

It is useful to remember that the antecedent is that part of the statement which is governed by the word 'if'.

Sometimes, however, we have the expression 'only if', and the inclusion of the word 'only' makes a difference. Let us consider the two statements:

1 If he wins the pools, then he will make a fortune
2 Only if he wins the pools will he make a fortune

Using 'W' for 'he wins the pools' and 'F' for 'he will make a fortune', the first statement is to be symbolised W ⊃ F. But the second cannot be symbolised in this way, for that would be to ignore the word 'only' which occurs in it. So let us see what difference the word 'only' makes.

The first statement:

If he wins the pools then he will make a fortune

states a sufficient condition of his making a fortune, but it does not state a necessary one. That is, it states *a* condition of his making a fortune, but it does not state that this is the *only* condition. He might not win the pools but still make a fortune. He might (successfully) rob a bank and make a fortune, or make an important invention.

The second statement:

Only if he wins the pools will he make a fortune

states that winning the pools is the only condition of his making a fortune. If he makes a fortune, it will be because he will have won the pools. We can see that the antecedent of this statement is 'He makes a fortune', and so the statement is to be symbolised: $F \supset W$. It is useful to remember that, while 'if' is the sign of the antecedent, the attachment of 'only' reverses it; 'only if' is a sign of the consequent.

Both 'if' and 'only if' must be distinguished from 'if and only if'. The third statement:

He will make a fortune if and only if he wins the pools

is different from:

If he wins the pools he will make a fortune

and from

Only if he wins the pools will he make a fortune.

Our third statement is a conjunction of the other two:

$$(W \supset F) . (F \supset W)$$

A way of seeing the difference between these three kinds of statement is to see what would falsify each of them.

1 If he wins the pools, he will make a fortune $(W \supset F)$

would be falsified if he won the pools but did not win a fortune; if he won the pools but, as all too often happens, the winnings amounted to very little. This would not falsify 2, but would falsify 3.

2 Only if he wins the pools will he make a fortune $(F \supset W)$

would be falsified if he made a fortune but did not win the pools. This would not falsify 1, but would falsify 3.

3   He will make a fortune if and only if he wins the pools (F ⊃ W) . (W ⊃ F)

would be false either if he won the pools but did not make a fortune, or if he made a fortune but did not win the pools.

We will give you more exercises in symbolising statements when we have introduced two further logical connectives in the next chapter.

12 Material Equivalence and Alternation

'. . . if and only if . . .' is one of our remaining logical constants to be explained. In order to show the differences between 'if', 'only if' and 'if and only if', we have symbolised the 'if and only if' statements as a conjunction of the other two. While this is not wrong, we do have a special symbol for 'if and only if', which is '≡', the sign for *material equivalence*. This logical connective too is placed between the two propositions it connects. Using this symbol, we should symbolise our statements:

He will make a fortune if and only if he wins the pools

as F ≡ W, which is read: His making a fortune is materially equivalent to his winning the pools.

This does indeed have the same meaning within our logical language as (F ⊃ W) . (W ⊃ F), as we shall explain in more detail in the next section, but it is the rule that we use this special symbol '≡', for 'if and only if'. This symbol is so defined that the compound is true when both components have the same truth value, but false otherwise. Below we give the definition for this connective:

p	q	$p \equiv q$
1	1	1
1	0	0
0	1	0
0	0	1

If we evaluate the form $F \equiv W$ in accordance with this definition, we shall see that it is false if he wins the pools but does not make a fortune, and false if he makes a fortune but does not win the pools, which is what we said above. (If you construct a truth table for $(F \supset W) . (W \supset F)$ you will see that the truth table of that statement form is exactly the same as that of $F \equiv W$.)

The definition of material equivalence, like the definition of material implication, has consequences which may seem odd. Just as any one statement materially implies another, except where the antecedent is true and the consequent false, so too, no matter what two statements may be, one statement is materially equivalent to another if they have the same truth values. This has the result that, since the two statements:

Lincoln was President of the USA

and:

Arsenic is poisonous

both have the same truth values, the one is materially equivalent to the other. A consequence of this definition is that it admits as materially equivalent statements which have nothing more in common than their truth values.

You may feel that this is unsatisfactory. It seems all right to say that two statements like:

Henry is a bachelor

and:

Henry is an unmarried man

are equivalent, but not to say that the two statements we gave above are equivalent. But it is important to remember that we are not saying that they are equivalent, but that they are *materially* equivalent. We give a special name to this special relation. We have to remember, that in truth-functional logic it is the truth values and not the subject matter which is important. As with material implication, as long as our definitions will allow the kinds of statement we ordinarily make, it will not matter if they also allow more. And to define material equivalence in this particular way is extremely useful for logical purposes.

The remaining symbol to be defined is that for *disjunction* usually expressed in English as 'either . . . or'.

The symbol for this logical connective is '$\vee$', known as the 'vel' * sign. Like the other connectives, it is placed between the two propositions it connects. The compound proposition:

Either Jones came or Smith came

is symbolised:

$$J \vee S$$

This symbol is so defined that the compound is true in every case except where both disjuncts are false. It is defined thus:

p	q	$p \vee q$
1	1	1
1	0	1
0	1	1
0	0	0

As you see, any proposition of the form $p \vee q$ is true in every case except where both components are false. It is true, not only when one is true and the other false, but also, when both are true.

In ordinary language, there are two ways in which we use the expression 'either . . . or . . .' Sometimes we use it in a way which accords with our definition, as for example, if someone says:

He either used bad materials or he was a poor workman.

* 'Vel' is a Latin word for 'or' which means 'either . . . or (and possibly both)'.

This is not intended to exclude the possibility that he *both* used bad materials *and* was a poor workman. The requirement that applicants should have qualifications either in mathematics or in English is not intended to exclude those applicants who have qualifications in both. Applicants should have one, or the other, or both. This sense of 'either . . . or . . .' is the *inclusive* sense, and it is in this way that we define the vel sign.

On the other hand, we do use the expression 'either . . . or' in the *exclusive* sense, when we mean one or the other but *not* both. In

I will pay the bill by cheque or by cash

it is used in the exclusive sense. Someone who makes this statement does not mean that he will pay either by cheque or by cash, or by *both*. An offer of tea or coffee is usually intended in the exclusive sense, of one or the other, but not both.

We could introduce another symbol for the exclusive sense of 'either . . . or . . .' and define it in such a way that the compound is true if one or other component is true, and false otherwise. This, however, is unnecessary, for the form of a statement using the exclusive sense can be symbolised using the symbols we already have. We may do this by writing:

$$(p . \sim q) \lor (\sim p . q)$$

Or, we may write:

$$\sim(p . q) . \sim(\sim p . \sim q)$$

thus denying the cases where both are true and both are false.

'Unless' is also to be understood as 'either . . . or . . .'.

For example:

Unless you hurry, we shall be late

means

Either you hurry or we shall be late

and it is symbolised:

$$p \lor q$$

'Neither . . . nor . . .' is the denial of 'either . . . or . . .'
and so should be symbolised: $\sim(p \lor q)$

As you will appreciate, if you are to acquire any facility
in logic you need plenty of practice, both in translating words
into symbols and in constructing truth-tables. The following
exercises will give you practice in translating statements into
symbols. Two of them cannot be translated using the symbols we have introduced. Explain why not.

Exercises

Translate into symbols:

1   If I work, I shall be rich. (W,R)
2   If I enjoy myself, I do not work. (E,W)
3   If I don't work, then I shall not be able to pay the rent. (W,P)
4   Either I earn money or I enjoy myself. (M,E)
5   I enjoy myself if and only if I do not work. (E,W)
6   Either Smith will come or Jones will come. (S,J)
7   Either I pay the rent and I don't buy a record, or I buy a
    record and don't pay the rent. (P,R)
8   Mary came to tea although John came. (M,J)
9   John and Mary came to tea. (M,J)
10 London and New York are large cities. (L,N)
11 London is larger than Manchester. (L,M)
12 James and John were disciples of Christ. (J,N)
13 James and John were brothers. (J,N)
14 He will pass his exam only if he works hard. (P,W)
15 He will make a great name for himself if he gets the part.
    (G,P)
16 Unless it stops raining there will be floods. (S,F)
17 If it doesn't rain soon, the harvest will be poor. (R,H)
18 Unless it rains soon, the harvest will be poor. (R,H)
19 The harvest will not be poor if and only if it rains soon.
    (H,R)
20 If nuclear power is not developed, there will be an energy
    crisis. (N,E)
21 Only if nuclear power is developed will there not be an
    energy crisis. (N,E)

22 If nuclear power is developed, there will not be an energy crisis but the environment will suffer. (N,E,S)

23 If this is an acid it tastes sour and turns litmus paper red. (A,S,L)

24 Only if this is an acid does it taste sour and turn litmus paper red. (A,S,L)

25 This is an acid if and only if it tastes sour and turns litmus paper red.

26 Either this is not an acid or it turns litmus red.

27 Either he won't get the part or he will make a great name for himself and be a rich man. (P,N,R)

28 If he gets the part, then if he makes a name for himself, he will be a rich man.

29 If the minister's financial dealings are made public, he will be prosecuted and disgraced. (F,P,D)

30 Either his financial dealings won't be made public or, if he is prosecuted, he will be imprisoned. (F,P,I)

13   Logical Equivalence

Now that we have given the definition of the triple bar, the symbol for material equivalence, we can explain the important notion of logical equivalence.

A statement of the form $p \equiv q$ is known as a bi-conditional. As we saw in the last section, the sign for material equivalence is so defined that the compound is true when the components have the same truth values but false otherwise. To assign truth values to a bi-conditional when the components are compound expressions, we follow the same procedure as hitherto; for example:

$$
\begin{array}{ccccccc}
(p & . & q) & \equiv & (\sim p & \vee & q) \\
1 & 1 & 1 & 1 & 0 & 1\,1 & 1 \\
1 & 0 & 0 & 1 & 0 & 1\,0 & 0 \\
0 & 0 & 1 & 0 & 1 & 0\,1 & 1 \\
0 & 0 & 0 & 0 & 1 & 0\,1 & 0 \\
(1) & & (4) & (2) & & (3) &
\end{array}
$$

When the bi-conditional expressing the material equivalence of two expressions is a logical truth (or *tautology*, as it is sometimes called), the two expressions are said to be *logically* equivalent. The two expressions in the above example are *not* logically equivalent; in the following example, they are:

$$(p \supset q) \equiv (\sim p \vee q)$$

1	1	1	1	0	1	1	1
1	0	0	1	0	1	0	0
0	1	1	1	1	0	1	1
0	1	0	1	1	0	1	0

(1)   (4) (2) (3)

As you can see from the column of ones under the main connective, however truth values are assigned to the simple propositions which make up the compound, the truth values of the expression on the left-hand side of the triple bar are exactly the same as those on the right-hand side. A statement having the form '$p \supset q$' is logically equivalent to a statement of the form '$\sim p \vee q$'.

This is perhaps obvious from ordinary English usage. For example, 'If it is foggy, John will be late' means the same as 'Either it won't be foggy or John will be late.' As we saw in the last section;

He will make a fortune if and only if he wins the pools

means the same as:

If he makes a fortune, then he wins the pools and if he wins the pools, then he makes a fortune

If you did as we suggested, you will have found that the two expressions have the same truth values. If you express the two as a bi-conditional:

$$(F \equiv W) \equiv [(F \supset W) \cdot (W \supset F)]$$

you will find that the result of applying the definition of material equivalence to the main connective is a column of ones, signifying that the two are logically equivalent.

It is not always as easy as this to see that two English expressions are logically equivalent. For example:

Either it won't be foggy or John will be late

means the same as:

It is false that it is foggy and John won't be late

Any statement of the form '$\sim p \lor q$' is logically equivalent to one of the form '$\sim(p \,.\, \sim q)$'. If you assign truth values, you will see that they are logically equivalent, the result being a column of ones under the main connective.

The following exercises, in which you are asked to detect logically equivalent expressions, will also give you practice in working with all the symbols for logical connectives that we have introduced.

Exercises

(A) Use truth-tables to determine which of the following are logically equivalent:

1   $(p \supset q) \equiv \sim(p \,.\, \sim q)$
2   $\sim(p \lor q) \equiv (p \supset q)$
3   $(p \,.\, q) \equiv \sim(\sim p \lor \sim q)$
4   $(p \,.\, q) \equiv \sim(p \supset \sim q)$
5   $(p \lor q) \equiv (\sim p \supset q)$
6   $(p \supset q) \equiv (q \supset p)$
7   $(p \supset q) \equiv (\sim q \supset \sim p)$
8   $(p \lor q) \equiv \sim(\sim p \,.\, \sim q)$
9   $\sim(p \,.\, q) \equiv (\sim p \lor \sim q)$
10   $(p \,.\, q) \equiv (\sim p \,.\, \sim q)$
11   $\{[(p \,.\, q) \,.\, (\sim p \,.\, q)] \,.\, (p \,.\, \sim q)\} \equiv (p \lor q)$
12   $(p \equiv q) \equiv [(p \,.\, q) \lor (\sim p \,.\, \sim q)]$

(B)   Which of the following propositions are logically equivalent to:

    If there is more rain next week the harvest will be bad.

  1   If the harvest is not bad, there will not be more rain next week.
  2   Either there won't be more rain next week or the harvest won't be bad.
  3   Either the harvest will be bad or there won't be more rain next week.
  4   It is false that the harvest will be bad and there won't be more rain next week.

(C)   Which of the following propositions are logically equivalent to:

If he is both ambitious and hard-working, then he will succeed.

1 If he does not succeed, then he is neither ambitious nor hard-working.
2 If he is not hard-working, then if he does not succeed, he is not ambitious.
3 If he does not succeed, then he is ambitious but not hard-working.
4 If he does not succeed and is ambitious, then he is not hard-working.
5 If he does not succeed, then either he is not ambitious or he is not hard-working.
6 If he is ambitious, then if he is hard-working, he will succeed.

14 A Short Cut to Truth-tables

So far the arguments and statements we have given you have had as their components either two or three simple propositions. But there are plenty which have more. We have seen that when we have two statements combined, there are four possibilities. When there are three statements combined there are eight possibilities. There are two values for any one statement: either it is true, or it is false. For two statements taken together there are 2^2 possibilities, that is: $2 \times 2 = 4$. For three statements taken together, there are 2^3 possibilities, that is: $2 \times 2 \times 2 = 8$. For four statements taken together there are 2^4 possibilities, that is: $2 \times 2 \times 2 \times 2 = 16$. And, in general, where n is the number of statements, 2^n is the number of possible combinations of truth values.

It is clear that to test the validity of arguments involving more than three simple statements will involve a great deal of time and paper. For one involving five, we should need thirty-two lines. Fortunately, once you can do ordinary truth-tables, we can use a shorter method. To use this method, however, you really need to know the definitions of the logical constants. Just as in arithmetic you know what 5×5 is, without having to refer to the five times table, so you hould now know, for example, what will be the truth values of any conjunction when both conjuncts are false, without needing to refer to the definition of the dot sign. If you do not yet know the definitions, you may continue to refer to them, but you will get on much quicker once you know them.

We shall explain the shorter truth-table method first, by using a familiar argument form which has only two variables. We have already seen that any argument, which when written as a material implication has the form:

$$[(p \supset q) \cdot p] \supset q$$

is valid. When we construct a truth-table, we find there is a column of ones under the main connective. No matter what truth values are assigned to the variables, the form will always have the truth value *true*. There is no instance of a true antecedent and a false consequent.

When we use the shorter method, we do not need to write out four lines or eight, or sixteen. We can work line by line, and we may not need to work more than one line. We begin by assuming that there *is* an instance of a true antecedent and a false consequent. If our assumption is incorrect, and the material implication is indeed a logical truth, we shall find that we cannot assign truth values to the remainder of the statement form without violating the rules we have laid down. We shall find that either we cannot assign truth values in accordance with the definitions, or that we cannot conform to the rule that each proposition has one and only one truth value. If our assumption is correct, that is, if there *is* an instance of a true antecedent and a false conclusion, then we *shall* be able to assign truth values in accordance with the rules we have laid down.

This abbreviation of the standard truth-table is sometimes called the *reductio ad absurdum* method. This phrase was originally used to refer to a method of argument first explained in Euclid's *Elements of Geometry* (a book which dates from the fourth century BC). In this method we assume the contradictory of what we have to prove. If this assumption results in a contradiction we know that what we are trying to prove does indeed follow from our premisses.

Thus, in the *reductio ad absurdum* test of a truth-table we assume that there is a zero in the main column of the truth-table under test. And this cannot happen if the argument form being tested is a valid one. (A variant of this method will be found useful later when we have to construct our own proofs.)

We write down our expression, with a zero under the main connective, to signify our assumption that the statement form is false.

Thus:

1   $[(p \supset q) . p] \supset q$

					0	

You will find it helpful to make 'boxes', one for each variable and constant, as we have done. In this way, you will be sure that you have assigned a truth value to each variable and each constant. The object is to work from this assumption, assigning truth values to each variable and constant, until it is quite clear, either that the assumption of falsity leads to a violation of the rules, in which case the assumption is incorrect, or that it does not.

We know from the definition that a material implication is false when the antecedent is true and the consequent is false, so we fill in 'true' under the main connective of the antecedent, which is the dot sign, and falsity under the consequent, which in this case is the variable '*q*'.

2   $[(p \supset q) . p] \supset q$

			1	0	0	

           1   2

Number each step underneath, as we have done, so that it is easier to check your working.

Again, we know from the definition that if a conjunction is true, both conjuncts are true, and so we write '1' for 'true' under the main connective on either side of the dot sign.

In this case, we write '1' under the hook sign on the left-hand side, and also under the variable '*p*' on the right.

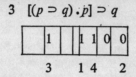

It now remains to deal with the first occurrence of *p* ⊃ *q*, which has the truth value 'true'. However, if a material implication is true, as this is, there are three possibilities: both antecedent and consequent may be true, the antecedent may be false and the consequent true, or both may be false. From the information that this material implication is true, we do not know what truth values to fill in for the variables, and it is not permitted to make an arbitrary choice. However, we do have the truth values of the variables at (4) and (2), so we are entitled to fill these in.

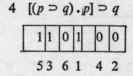

We now have a truth value under every constant and every variable, working from the assumption that this material implication is false. But you will see that the material implication (*p* ⊃ *q*) has the truth value 'true', yet it has a true antecedent and a false consequent. (5, 3, 6, above.) This is *not* in accordance with the definition of the hook sign. The assumption that this statement form is false, thus leads to a violation of the rules. But in that case, the assumption is incorrect, and so we can say that this compound statement form is true and the argument which was written as a material implication is valid. In other words, were we to construct the full truth-table there would be no zeros in the column under the main connective. Indicate the violation and do not forget to write 'valid' by the side.

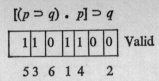

$$[(p \supset q) \cdot p] \supset q$$

| 1 | 1 | 0 | 1 | 1 | 0 | 0 | Valid |

5 3 6 1 4   2

Any argument can be tested for validity by the shorter truth-table method. As before, symbolise the argument, using abbreviatory letters, and write it as a material implication, and then follow the procedure given above. Here is another example:

$$[(A \lor B) \cdot (B \cdot C)] \supset B$$

Step 1   Write out the form with a box underneath for each variable and each constant:

$$[(A \lor B) \cdot (B \cdot C)] \supset B$$

Step 2   Assume the statement form is false. Write 0 under the main connective:

$$[(A \lor B) \cdot (B \cdot C)] \supset B$$

| | | | | | | | 0 | |

Step 3   When a material implication is false, the antecedent is true and the consequent false. Fill in these truth values and number the boxes:

$$[(A \lor B) \cdot (B \cdot C)] \supset B$$

| | | | 1 | | | 0 | 0 |

       1   2

Step 4   When a conjunction is true (1) both conjuncts are true. Fill in these truth values. (3,4)

$$[(A \lor B) . (B . C)] \supset B$$

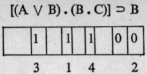

3   1   4   2

Step 5   As there are three possible ways in which a disjunction may be true, we leave that for now, and
deal with (4). When a conjunction is true, both
conjuncts are true, so fill in these truth values. (5,6)

$$[(A \lor B) . (B . C)] \supset B$$

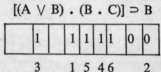

3   1 5 46   2

We need go no further. For, in filling in truth values
according to the definitions, on the assumption that the
statement form is false, we have assigned contradictory
values to 'B'. At 5, 'B' is true, and at 2, it is false. But this
violates the rule that each variable has one and only one
truth value. Thus the assumption that this statement form
is false leads to a violation of the rules. The assumption is
incorrect, and the statement form is valid. Indicate the
violation, and write 'Valid' by the side:

$$[(A \lor B) . (B . C)] \supset B$$

| | 1 | | 1 | 1 | 1 | 1 | 0 | 0 | Valid

3   1 5 4 6   2

We will do one more before giving you some to try
yourself.

$$\{[(L \lor M) \supset N] . N\} \supset (L \lor M)$$

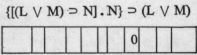

Step 3   When a material implication is false, the antecedent
is true and the consequent is false. Watch the

brackets here. It is the whole of the expression in braces which is the antecedent.

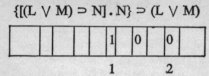

Step 4   At (1) we have a true conjunction, so both conjuncts are true. Again, watch the brackets. The conjuncts are the whole expression within square brackets on the left-hand side of the dot sign, and N on the right.

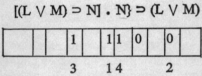

Step 5   As there are three possible ways of filling in the truth values on either side of 3, ignore this for the time being. We *can* fill in the truth values on either side of the disjunction at (2). This is false, and there is only one possibility for a false disjunction: both disjuncts are false.
Fill in the values:

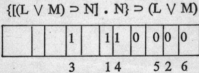

Step 6   We have values for L, M and N, so fill in these in the antecedent:

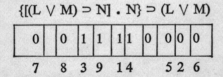

Step 7   Only one truth value remains to be assigned: to '∨' in the first occurrence of L ∨ M. Since both disjuncts are false, the whole must be false. Fill in this value:

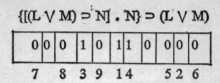

In assigning truth values on the assumption that this statement form is false, we have *not* violated any of the rules. Accordingly, our assumption is correct. That is to say, were we to construct the *full* truth-table, there would be at least one zero in the main column. The statement form is one in which there can be a true antecedent and a false conclusion. The argument form which was written as a material implication is invalid, for it can, as we have shown, have true premisses and a false conclusion.

The shorter truth-table method, as you see, is much quicker and uses far less paper than the ordinary truth-table method. But you do need to know the definitions and to keep a sharp eye out for any violations. Remember that you may *not* assign truth values in an arbitrary fashion.

Now do the following exercises.

Exercises

Use the shorter truth-table method to test the validity of the following abbreviated arguments:

1   [(A ∨ B) . A] ⊃ B
2   [(P ⊃ Q) ⊃ R] ⊃ [(P . Q) ⊃ R]
3   [(P ⊃ Q) . (Q ⊃ P)] ⊃ (P ⊃ P)
4   [(P ⊃ Q) . Q] ⊃ P
5   [(A ⊃ B) . A] ⊃ A
6   [(P ⊃ Q) . (Q ⊃ R)] ⊃ (P ⊃ R)
7   [(Q ⊃ P) . (R ⊃ P)] ⊃ (Q ⊃ R)
8   [(P ⊃ Q) . P] ⊃ (Q ∨ R)

9   $[(P \supset Q) \supset R] \supset [(R \supset P) \supset (J \supset P)$

10 $\{[(Q \lor R) \supset P] . Q\} \supset P$

11 $\{[(Q \lor R) \supset P] . R\} \supset (P \supset J)$

12 $\{[(A \lor B) \supset C] . [(C \lor D) \supset E]\} \supset (B \supset E)$

Negation in the Short
Truth-table Method

In the exercises you have just done, there were no negation
signs. Using the shorter truth-table method on forms which
include negation signs presents no great difficulty, but you
must make quite sure *which* forms are negated. We will do
two examples by way of illustration.

$$[(F \supset G) . (\sim F \supset H)] \supset (\sim G \supset H)$$

Steps 1, 2 and 3

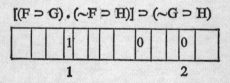

(Notice the separate boxes for each of the two
negation signs.)

Step 4 The conjuncts at (1) are the two expressions on
either side, and since the conjunction is true, the
conjuncts are true:

$$[(F \supset G) \cdot (\sim F \supset H)] \supset (\sim G \supset H)$$

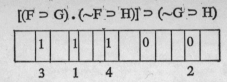

	1		1		1		0		0	
	3		1		4				2	

Step 5   Reading from left to right, we see that we cannot yet fill in the first two material implications, for both are true, and we have no reason to fill in one of the three possibilities rather than another. We therefore begin with the consequent, for here we have a false material implication. But please notice that the antecedent here is not G, but the *negation* of G:

$$[(F \supset G) \cdot (\sim F \supset H)] \supset (\sim G \supset H)$$

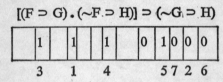

	1		1		1		0	1	0	0	0
	3		1		4			5	7	2	6

Step 6   Since the *negation* of G is true, G will be false:

$$[(F \supset G) \cdot (\sim F \supset H)] \supset (\sim G \supset H)$$

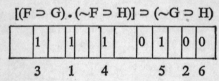

	1		1		1		0	1		0	0
	3		1		4			5		2	6

Step 7   We can now fill in the values for G and H in the antecedent.

$$[(F \supset G) \cdot (\sim F \supset H)] \supset (\sim G \supset H)$$

	1	0	1		1	0		0	1	0	0	0
	3	8	1		4	9		5	7	2	6

Step 8   We now have enough information to complete the first material implication which occurs: F ⊃ G. As this is true, with a false consequent, the antecedent F must also be false:

[(F ⊃ G) . (~F ⊃ H)] ⊃ (~G ⊃ H)

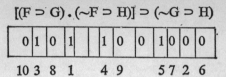

0	1	0	1		1	0	0	1	0	0	0

10 3 8 1   4 9   5 7 2 6

Step 9   We now have the value for F, which we can fill in wherever it occurs. As this is false, its negation is true.

[(F ⊃ G) . (~F ⊃ H)] ⊃ (~G ⊃ H)

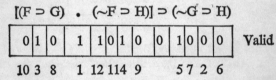

| 0 | 1 | 0 | | 1 | 1 | 0 | 1 | 0 | | 0 | 1 | 0 | 0 | 0 | **Valid**
|---|---|---|---|---|---|---|---|---|---|---|---|---|---|---|

10 3 8   1 12 114 9   5 7 2 6

But now, this gives a true antecedent (12) and a false conclusion (9) for a material implication which is true (4). The rules are violated. The argument is valid.

Now consider the following which is a little more complicated, in that it includes not just negated variables, but a negated form.

[(D ⊃ E) . ~(~E ∨ ~F)] ⊃ E

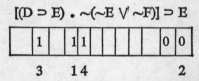

	1		1	1						0	0

3   14   2

Since we have a true conjunction (at 1), we may fill in the truth values true on either side. But please notice that, while on the left-hand side the one goes under the hook sign, to show that the whole expression 'D ⊃ E' is true, on the right-hand side it goes under the first occurrence of the negation sign. It is the *negation* of '~E ∨ ~F' which is conjoined with 'D ⊃ E'.

Since the negation of the whole expression contained within the round brackets (~E ∨ ~F) is true, the expression

itself must be false, and so we write 0 under the vel sign.
The alternates here are the *negation* of E and the negation
of F, so be sure to write falsity under the negation signs,
and not under E and F. As the negation of E, and the
negation of F are both false, E will be true, and F will be
true.

We do not need to proceed further, for the rules have been
violated. At (8) E has the truth value 'true', but at (2) the
truth value 'false'.

Exercises

Check the validity of the following argument-forms by the shorter
truth-table method:

1   (P ⊃ Q) ⊃ (~Q ⊃ ~P)
2   [(P ⊃ Q) . ~Q] ⊃ ~P
3   [(P ⊃ Q) . ~P] ⊃ ~Q
4   [(P ⊃ Q) . (~R ⊃ ~Q)] ⊃ (~R ⊃ ~P)
5   [(P . Q) ⊃ R] ⊃ [(Q . ~R) ⊃ ~P]
6   [A ⊃ (B ⊃ C)] ⊃ [B ⊃ (~C ⊃ ~A)]
7   [(~P ∨ Q) . (~Q ∨ R)] ⊃ (~P ∨ R)
8   [(P ⊃ Q) ⊃ R] ⊃ [P ⊃ (Q ∨ R)]
9   [(P ⊃ Q) ⊃ R] ⊃ [(P . Q) ⊃ R]
10 [(P . Q) ⊃ R] ⊃ [~(Q ⊃ P) ⊃ R]
11 (A ∨ ~B) ⊃ (B ⊃ A)
12 [~B ⊃ (A . C)] ⊃ [~C ∨ ~A) ⊃ B]

16 More on Shorter Truth-tables

You can see that the shorter truth-table method does indeed merit its name. We must, however, sound a word of caution. Sometimes it may be necessary to use more than one line.

Consider the following example, which we have worked as far as possible, without making any arbitrary moves:

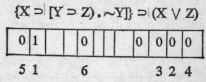

How are we to proceed? We do not have a value for Y. We do not know the truth value of the expression within the square brackets, which is the consequent of the first hook sign. We have truth here, but with a false antecedent. A material implication with a false antecedent is true, whether it has a false or a true consequent. So, we do not know what truth value to fill in under the dot sign. There are two possibilities for Y ⊃ Z. A material implication with a false consequent will be true, if the antecedent is false, and false if the antecedent is true. But we have no truth value for the antecedent, and so no reason to fill in one truth value rather than another.

Since we may not make any arbitrary move, we must be prepared to try both possibilities: that Y ⊃ Z is true, and that Y ⊃ Z is false. Or, which comes to the same thing in this example, we could be prepared to try both possible values for the variable Y. Let us first try assigning truth to the compound (Y ⊃ Z).

$$\{X \supset [(Y \supset Z) \cdot \sim Y]\} \supset (X \vee Z)$$

0	1		1	0				0	0	0	0
5	1		7	6				3	2	4	

This gives us the truth value for Y. Since the compound is true, with a false consequent, the antecedent must be false.

Below we have filled in the value for Y:

$$\{X \supset [(Y \supset Z) \cdot \sim Y]\} \supset (X \vee Z)$$

0	1		0	1	0		1	0		0		0	0	0
5	1		8	7	6		10	9				3	2	4

The values on both sides of the conjunction sign are true (7,10) so the conjunction is true:

$$\{X \supset [(Y \supset Z) \cdot \sim Y]\} \supset (X \vee Z)$$

0	1		0	1	0		1	1	0		0		0	0	0
5	1		8	7	6		11	10	9				3	2	4

No rules have been violated. The material implication at 1, is true, and has, correctly, a false antecedent (5) and a true consequent (11).

In this case, we do not need to try the second possibility, for the first that we tried has shown the possibility of this material implication's having a true antecedent and a false conclusion. The abbreviated argument which has been written as a material implication can have true premisses and a false conclusion. It is therefore invalid.

Suppose, however, that when we had tried the first possibility, there was a violation of the rules. This would not have shown that there was no possible way of assigning truth values which would give true premisses and a false conclusion. We should not have shown that until we had tried every possible way.

There is another important point to remember in using truth-tables, whether you construct the full table or use the shorter *reductio ad absurdum* method. There will often be more than two premisses in the argument and all the premisses have to be joined by conjunction. For example, suppose we have:

$$\begin{array}{ll} 1 & P \supset Q \\ 2 & Q \supset R \\ 3 & {\sim}S \supset {\sim}R \end{array}$$

Therefore: $P \supset S$

We set this out for truth-tabling as:

$$[(P \supset Q) . (Q \supset R) . ({\sim}S \supset {\sim}R)] \supset (P \supset S)$$

Which is the main connective of the two dot-signs to the left of the principal hook sign? The answer is that it does not matter which you take, provided that your bracketing shows which you have chosen. Thus:

A $[(P \supset Q) . \{(Q \supset R) . ({\sim}S \supset {\sim}R)\}] \supset (P \supset S)$

or

B $[\{(P \supset Q) . (Q \supset R)\} . ({\sim}S \supset {\sim}R)] \supset (P \supset S)$

In the first case, A, the first dot is the main connective *of the premisses*. In B, it is the second.

Thus in A, you will proceed:

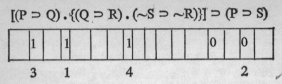

And in B, you will proceed:

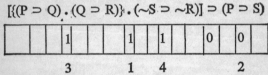

The result is normally the same, though it might happen that one grouping would lead to an ambiguity of the type discussed above (on p. 95). In that case, it would be sensible to choose the other grouping. Where there are more than three premisses, the possible groupings are, of course, more numerous but proper bracketing will prevent mistakes.

Exercises on Part I

(A) Test the following expressions by truth-tables using either the full table or the short method. (It is best not to use the full truth-table for expressions involving more than three variables.)

1   $[(P \supset Q) . (\sim P \supset R)] \supset (\sim Q \supset R)$
2   $[(P \supset Q) \supset R] \supset [P \supset (Q \supset R)]$
3   $[(\sim P \supset \sim Q) \supset \sim R] \supset [R \supset (\sim Q \supset \sim P)$
4   $[(\sim P \supset R) . (\sim Q \supset R)] \supset [(P \vee Q) \vee R]$
5   $\{[A \supset (B \vee C)] . \sim C\} \supset (\sim B \supset \sim A)$
6   $\{[M \supset (P \vee L)] . P\} \supset (M \supset \sim L)$
7   $\{P \supset [(Q . R) . \sim R]\} \supset \sim P$
8   $\{X \supset [(Y \supset Z) . \sim Y]\} \supset (X \vee Z)$
9   $\{P \supset [(R \supset Q) . Q]\} \supset (P \supset R)$
10 $\{[P \supset (Q \supset R)] \supset \sim R\} \supset (Q \supset \sim P)$
11 $[P \supset (P \vee Q)] \supset \{[\sim Q \supset (P \supset P)] . [\sim P \supset (P \supset Q)]\}$
12 $P \supset [Q \supset \sim (P \supset \sim Q)]$
13 $[(P \supset Q) \supset Q] \supset (\sim P \vee Q)$
14 $\{P \supset [Q \supset (P \supset R)]\} \supset [(P . Q) \supset R]$

15 [(P ⊃ Q) ⊃ (P ⊃ R)] ⊃ {P ⊃ [(P ⊃ Q) ⊃ R]}
16 [(A . ~B) ⊃ C] ⊃ [(C . B) ⊃ ~A]
17 [(~P ⊃ R) . (~Q ⊃ R)] ⊃ [(P ∨ Q) ∨ R]
18 {[(P ⊃ Q) . (S ⊃ ~R)] . [~(~P ∨ S) . (Q ⊃ R)]} ⊃ T
19 P ⊃ [(P . Q) ∨ (P . ~Q)]
20 {[A ⊃ (B ⊃ C)] . [(A ⊃ C) ⊃ D] . (B ⊃ E)} ⊃
    [B ⊃ (D . E)]
21 {[(Q . R) ⊃ S] . [(R ⊃ S) ⊃ T]} ⊃ (~T ⊃ ~Q)
22 [~(P ⊃ Q) ⊃ (R ⊃ ~S)] ⊃ [(P . R) ⊃ (S ⊃ Q)]
23 [P ⊃ (Q . R)] ⊃ {[Q ⊃ (S . T)] ⊃ (P ⊃ S)}
24 [(P . Q) ⊃ R] ⊃ [(Q . ~R) ⊃ ~P]
25 {A ⊃ [B ⊃ (C ⊃ D)]} ⊃ {C ⊃ [B ⊃ (A ⊃ D)]}
26 [(A . ~B) ⊃ C] ⊃ [(B . ~C) ⊃ ~A]
27 [(F . G) ⊃ H] ⊃ [G ⊃ (~H ⊃ ~F)]
28 [(P ⊃ Q) ⊃ ~R] ⊃ [R ⊃ (~P ∨ ~Q)]
29 [A ⊃ (B . ~A)] . [(A ⊃ B) . (~A ⊃ ~B)] ⊃ [A ⊃
    (A . B)]
30 {[A ⊃ (B . C)] . [C ⊃ (D ⊃ E)] . ~(D ⊃ ~A)} ⊃
    (B ⊃ E)
31 {[(P . Q) ⊃ ~R] . (S ⊃ R) . [(S ⊃ V) ⊃ T] .
    ~(P ⊃ ~Q)} ⊃ (~T ⊃ R)
32 [~(~P ∨ Q) ⊃ (R ⊃ ~S)] ⊃ [(P . R) ⊃ (S ⊃ Q)]
33 {(B ∨ A) . [(C . B) ⊃ ~D] . ~(D ⊃ A)} ⊃ ~C
34 {[A ⊃ (B ⊃ C)] . [(A ⊃ C) ⊃ D] . (B ⊃ E)} ⊃
    [B ⊃ (D . E)]
35 (A ⊃ B) ≡ (~A ∨ B)
36 [(P ⊃ Q) ⊃ R] ≡ [(P . Q) ⊃ R]
37 [(P ≡ Q) . (~R ∨ Q) . R] ⊃ P
38 {P ≡ [(Q ∨ R) . ~(Q ∨ R)]} ⊃ ~P
39 ~(P ∨ Q) ≡ (~P . ~Q)
40 (P ≡ Q) ≡ [(P ⊃ Q) . (Q ⊃ P)]
41 (P ≡ Q) ≡ [(P . Q) ∨ (~P . ~Q)]
42 [(P . Q) ⊃ R) ≡ [P ⊃ (Q ⊃ R)]
43 [P . (Q ∨ R)] ≡ [(P . Q) ∨ (P . R)]
44 [P ∨ (Q . R)] ≡ [(P ∨ Q) . (P ∨ R)]

(B) Put the following arguments into logical notation and test
them for validity by truth-table methods:

1 Either he is guilty or he has been framed. If the police
   haven't been bribed, then he hasn't been framed. If
   the police have been bribed, then the Home Secretary
   will refuse a public enquiry. Therefore, if the Home

Secretary does not refuse a public enquiry, he is guilty. (G,F,B,R)

2 If the Prime Minister resigns and there is a general election, then the opposition will be returned and foreign relations will improve. If there is a general election, then foreign relations won't improve. *Therefore:* either there won't be a general election or the Prime Minister won't resign. (R,E,O,I)

3 If the government approves the report and the press is favourable, then the speed limit will be raised. If the speed limit is raised, then road casualties will increase and there will be a public outcry. There will not be a public outcry. *Therefore:* If the government approves the report, the press will not be favourable.(A,P,S,C,O)

4 Either I camp or I go to a hotel. If I camp then I must buy a tent. If I buy a tent, I shall be unable to pay the rent. Either I am able to pay the rent or I shall have an overdraft. *Therefore:* I shall have an overdraft. (C,H,T,A,O)

5 If it is false that prices will rise and taxes will not be reduced, then there will be increased spending. If there is increased spending, then there will be a fall in national savings. There won't be a fall in national savings. *Therefore:* it is false that either prices will not rise or taxes will be reduced.

6 If A's evidence is true, then B is not guilty. If B is not guilty, then C's evidence is perjured. *Therefore,* if C's evidence is not perjured, A's evidence is not true.

7 If there is a change of government, confidence in the pound will be restored. If imports are restricted, confidence in the pound will not be restored. Imports will be restricted. *Therefore:* There will not be a change of government.

8 If A beats B, then if he beats C he will also beat D and win the cup. He will beat C but he won't beat D. *Therefore:* A won't beat B.

9 If the picture is not a forgery, then it is valuable. It is not the case that either it is a forgery or that it is not sought after by collectors. If the picture is not by Vermeer, then it is not sought after by collectors. *Therefore:* the picture is valuable and it is by Vermeer.

10 If the patient takes penicillin and is properly looked after, then he will recover. If he recovers, then his relatives will be disappointed. His relatives will not be disappointed. *Therefore:* if he takes penicillin, he won't be properly looked after.

11 If Jones is guilty or the police are suspicious, then either he will bribe the police or he will not remain in the country. *Therefore:* if Jones remains in the country or the police are suspicious, then, if he is guilty, he will bribe the police.

12 If Jones is elected, Smith will resign. If Brown is elected, then Smith won't resign. If Jones is elected, then Smith won't be elected. *Therefore:* Smith will resign.

13 If Jones is elected, Smith will resign. If Brown is elected, Smith will not resign. *Therefore:* If Jones is elected, Brown is not elected.

14 If the price of gold shares falls, or boring operations fail, then either Jones will go bankrupt or he will commit suicide. If boring operations fail or Jones goes bankrupt, there will be a prosecution. There will not be a prosecution. The price of gold shares will fall. *Therefore:* Jones will commit suicide.

15 If the price of gold shares falls or boring operations fail, then either Jones will go bankrupt or he will commit suicide. If Jones goes bankrupt or boring operations fail, there will be a prosecution. If the price of gold shares falls, there will be a prosecution. There won't be a prosecution. *Therefore:* Either Jones will go bankrupt or he will commit suicide.

16 If there is an election, the government will not remain in power. Either the government won't remain in power or there will be a *coup d'état*. There won't be a *coup d'état*. *Therefore:* Either there won't be an election or the Prime Minister will be arrested.

17 If the police hear of the Prime Minister's activities, then if he refuses to share the profits, there will be a public scandal. If he does not refuse to share the profits, then the press will have to be silenced. There will not be a public scandal, and the press will not have to be silenced. But the police will hear of the Prime Minister's activities. *Therefore:* there will be a general election.

18 If John divorces Ellen, then, if he is stupid, he will marry Ann. Either he won't remain sane or he will divorce Ellen. John is stupid. *Therefore:* If he remains sane, he will marry Ann.

19 If the evidence was forged or the police are bribed, then A is not guilty. If the chief witness was not telling the truth, then the evidence was forged. If the chief witness was telling the truth, then A is guilty. The evidence was not forged. *Therefore:* The police are not bribed.

Part II

The Logic of Statements (2)

1 Decision procedures and proofs

So far, you have learned how to test a logical formula to see whether or not it expresses a logical truth. And by far the most important practical application of this technique is to set out an argument in the form of a complex 'if . . . then' statement, where the antecedent is a premiss or a conjunction of premisses and the consequent is the conclusion. If this 'if . . . then' statement turns out to be a logical truth, we know for sure that the argument is valid.

This technique is known as a *decision procedure* or *decision method*. Truth-tables are one example of a decision procedure but there are others. (See the Bibliography at the end of the book for reading on other decision procedures.) These methods are very useful where we are given an argument which can be dealt with at the level of the logic of propositions. In the truth-table, we have a purely mechanical device for settling the question 'Valid or not?' quite decisively. In fact, this sort of calculation can be carried out very effectively on a computer. But truth-tables (or other decision methods) are not the whole of logic, even at the level of the logic of propositions. Suppose we are given a set of premisses and are asked what follows from the premisses. Or suppose, we are given an argument with premises and conclusion and are asked not just whether it is a valid argument but rather we are asked to show how the conclusion can be deducted from the premises. Truth-tables will not give us much help with such questions. Of course, if we know an argument not to be a valid one, we are excused from answering the question 'How can the conclusion be deduced?' It cannot be deduced if the argument is invalid. However, we often are faced with problems in propositional logic of a kind that truth-tables cannot solve for us. And for these problems we need other methods. We need to know how to construct formal proofs.

In a formal proof, each line is either a premiss, or is deduced from the premises by a rule of inference. The last line is the conclusion. Suppose we wish to prove that the following argument is valid:

If Tom wins the contest, then Dick is runner up. Either Dick is runner up or Harry comes last. But Dick is not runner up. Therefore, Harry is last and Tom does not win the contest.

First, we symbolise the argument, and set it out with each premiss numbered and each on a separate line. The conclusion to be proved is set out to the side:

$$1 \quad T \supset D$$
$$2 \quad D \lor H$$
$$3 \quad {\sim}D \qquad /\therefore H \, . \, {\sim}T$$

We are to deduce the conclusion, which will be the last line of the proof, using a rule of inference.

As rules of inference, we use elementary valid argument forms, and logically equivalent expressions. First, we will give the elementary valid argument forms. All of these can be shown to be valid by truth-table methods, and as we go along, you should demonstrate for yourself that they are valid.

1   *Modus ponens* (MP)
$$p \supset q$$
$$p$$
$$\therefore q$$

2   *Modus tollens* (MT)
$$p \supset q$$
$$\sim q$$
$$\therefore \sim p$$

3   Constructive Dilemma (CD)
$$(p \supset q) \cdot (r \supset s)$$
$$p \lor r$$
$$\therefore q \lor s$$

4   Destructive Dilemma (DD)
$$(p \supset q) \cdot (r \supset s)$$
$$\sim q \lor \sim s$$
$$\therefore \sim p \lor \sim r$$

5   Disjunctive Syllogism (DS)
$$p \lor q$$
$$\sim p$$
$$\therefore q$$

6   Hypothetical Syllogism (HS)
$$p \supset q$$
$$q \supset r$$
$$\therefore p \supset r$$

7   Simplification (Simp.)
$$p \cdot q$$
$$\therefore p$$

8   Addition (Add.)
$$p$$
$$\therefore p \lor q$$

9   Conjunction (Conj.)
$$p$$
$$q$$
$$\therefore p \cdot q$$

You should keep a copy of these rules by you, for you will need to refer to them constantly.

1 The *Modus ponens* rule is understood in the following way: if $p \supset q$ is a line in a proof, and p is a line in a proof, then from those two lines we may infer q. The others are similarly understood. Below, we give the completed proof of the argument given above:

$$
\begin{array}{lll}
1 & T \supset D & \\
2 & D \lor H & \\
3 & \sim D & /\therefore H \cdot \sim T \\
4 & H & 2,3,DS \\
5 & \sim T & 1,3,MT \\
6 & H \cdot \sim T & 4,5,Conj.
\end{array}
$$

Line 4 has been inferred from lines 2 and 3 by the Disjunctive Syllogism rule. Notice that beside line 4 we have written the numbers of the lines from which it has been inferred, and the name of the rule by which it has been inferred. Line 5 has been inferred from lines 1 and 3 by the *Modus tollens* rule, and on line 6, we have conjoined lines 4 and 5 in accordance with the Conjunction rule.

In order to help you to become familiar with the rules, we give some almost completed formal proofs. In all of these, lines 1 and 2 (or line 1) are premisses, and the last line is the conclusion. The last line has been deduced from the preceding line(s) by one rule of inference. You are required to say which rule of inference has been used. We have completed the first one for you.

Exercises

1   (1) A ⊃ C
     (2) A   /∴ C
     (3) C   1,2,MP

2   (1) R   /∴ R ∨ S
     (2) R ∨ S   1,

3   (1) (S ⊃ J) . (R ⊃ B)
     (2) ~J ∨ ~B   /∴ ~S ∨ ~R
     (3) ~S ∨ ~R   1,2,

4   (1) R ⊃ W
     (2) W ⊃ U   /∴ R ⊃ U
     (3) R ⊃ U   1,2,

5   (1) A ⊃ C
     (2) ~C   /∴ ~A
     (3) ~A   1,2,

6   (1) (S ⊃ J) . (R ⊃ B)
     (2) S ∨ R   /∴ J ∨ B
     (3) J ∨ . B   1,2,

7   (1) R
     (2) T   /∴ R . T
     (3) R . T   1,2,

8   (1) R ∨ S
     (2) ~R   /∴ S
     (3) S   1,2,

9   (1) M . N   /∴ M

      (2) M   1,

10 (1) R ⊃ Q

      (2) ∼Q   /∴ ∼R

      (3) ∼R   1,2,

2   The rules of inference apply, of course, to more complicated abbreviated arguments. Here is an example:

      1   (H . M) ⊃ (Z ∨ Q)

      2   H . M   /∴ Z ∨ Q

      3   Z ∨ Q   1,2,MP

In this example, line 3, (the conclusion) is deduced from lines 1 and 2 by the *Modus ponens* rule. Line 1 is a substitution instance of $p ⊃ q$, and line 2 is a substitution instance of p. According to the *Modus ponens* rule, if there is a line in a proof with the form $p ⊃ q$, and a line which affirms the antecedent, we may deduce the consequent.

Here is another example:

      1   (L ≡ M) ∨ (Z . O)

      2   ∼(L ≡ M)   /∴ Z . O

      3   Z . O   1,2,DS

The conclusion has been deduced from the premises by the Disjunctive Syllogism rule. Line 1 is a substitution instance of $p ∨ q$, and line 2 is a substitution instance of $∼p$. The rule permits the deduction of the substitution instance of q, in this case, Z . O.

In order to be able to apply the rules, you need to be able to recognise substitution instances. Do not allow yourself to be confused by the number of abbreviatory letters and brackets in an example. The line [(Z . O) ∨ (L ⊃ M)] ∨ [(X ∨ J) ⊃ (L ≡ M)] is a substitution instance of $p ∨ q$: it consists of two abbreviated compound statements connected by ∨.

Here are some examples of formal proofs in which the rules of inference have been applied to more complicated examples. As before, you are required to state which rule has been used, and in some cases, to deduce the conclusion.

Exercises

1   (1) $(Z \supset L) \lor (P . V)$
    (2) $\sim(Z \supset L)$ $/\therefore P . V$
    (3) $P . V$ 1,2,

2   (1) $(L \equiv N) . (B \lor A)$ $/\therefore L \equiv N$
    (2) $(L \equiv N)$ 1,

3   (1) C $/\therefore C \lor [(M . R) \lor (N . O)]$
    (2) $C \lor [(M . R) \lor (N . O)]$ 1,

4   (1) $(V \lor W) \supset (A . B)$
    (2) $\sim(A . B)$ $/\therefore \sim(V \lor W)$
    (3)   1,2,

5   (1) $[(A . B) \supset C] . [(F \lor D) \supset L]$
    (2) $(A . B) \lor (F \lor D)$ $/\therefore C \lor L$
    (3)   1,2,

6   (1) $[(A . B) \lor C] \supset (F . G)$
    (2) $(A . B) \lor C$ $/\therefore F . G$
    (3)   1,2,

7   (1) $[(H \lor J) \supset (L . M)] . [(N . V) \supset (Z . Q)]$
    (2) $\sim(L . M) \lor \sim(Z . Q)$ $/\therefore \sim(H \lor J) \lor \sim(N . V)$
    (3) $\sim(H \lor J) \lor \sim(N . V)$ 1,2,

8   (1) $L \supset (M . F)$
    (2) $(M . F) \supset P$ $/\therefore L \supset P$
    (3)   1,2,

9   (1) $Z \lor K$
    (2) $F \supset G$ $/\therefore (Z \lor K) . (F \supset G)$
    (3) $(Z \lor K) . (F \supset G)$ 1,2,

3 Unlike the construction of truth-tables, the construction of a formal proof is not a mechanical procedure. We cannot, therefore, give you a set of instructions to follow. We can only give you hints as to the best way to proceed, and describe the way in which we would do so. It is best to look first at the conclusion, and then at the lines given, to see how the conclusion could be deduced. Here is an example:

    1 $(A \supset B) . (C \supset D)$
    2 $\sim B$ $/\therefore \sim A$

We note that we have A ⊃ B as part of the first line, and ~B is the second line. *If* we had A ⊃ B as a line in the proof, we could derive ~A by the *Modus tollens* rule. But we do not have A ⊃ B as a line in the proof, and we may not apply any of these nine rules of inference to part of a line. We note that the first line is a substitution instance of *p . q*, and we know that the simplification rule allows us to drop the second conjunct. By using the simplification rule, we deduce A ⊃ B as the third line in the proof. From that and ~B, which is line 2, we can derive ~A by the *Modus tollens* rule:

$$
\begin{array}{lll}
1 & (A \supset B) . (C \supset D) & \\
2 & \sim B & /\therefore \sim A \\
3 & A \supset B & 1, \text{Simp.} \\
4 & \sim A & 3, 2, \text{MT}
\end{array}
$$

Now try the following exercises. Each example requires the use of two rules in order to deduce the conclusion. When you have added another line to the ones you are given, you may also use that to deduce the conclusion.

Exercises

1 (1) T . S   /∴ T ∨ U
2 (1) (J ⊃ K) . (L ⊃ M)
   (2) J   /∴ K ∨ M
3 (1) A ⊃ B
   (2) C ⊃ D
   (3) ~B ∨ ~D   /∴ ~A ∨ ~C
4 (1) (D ∨ S) . (F ⊃ G)
   (2) ~D   /∴ S
5 (1) (A ⊃ B) ∨ (L ⊃ H)
   (2) ~(A ⊃ B)
   (3) L   /∴ H
6 (1) (P ⊃ Q) . (R ⊃ S)
   (2) ~Q   /∴ ~P
7 (1) [P ⊃ (Q . R)] . [(Q . R) ⊃ S]
   (2) ~S   /∴ ~P
8 (1) [(F ∨ ~J) ⊃ (P . M)] . [(B . V) ⊃ (K . Q)]
   (2) ~(P . M)

    (3) (F ∨ ∼J) ∨ (B . V) /∴ K . Q

9 (1) [(Z ∨ S) ⊃ (T . Y)] . [(M ∨ N) ⊃ (O . P)]
    (2) Q
    (3) ∼(T . Y) ∨ ∼(O . P)

                      /∴.[∼(Z ∨ S) ∨ ∼(M ∨ N)] . Q

10 (1) [J ∨ (V ⊃ Z)] ⊃ (∼P ∨ T)
    (2) J   /∴ ∼P ∨ T

4 The rules must be very carefully observed. Make quite
sure that each step is permitted by one or other of the rules.
Suppose, for example, that you have (D . E) . P as a line in a
proof, and you wish to derive D. There is no rule which
allows the deduction of D in one step. The simplification rule
must be used twice. (D . E) . P is a substitution instance of
p . q from which the simplification rule permits the deduction
of the first conjunct. The first conjunct in our example is D . E.
The simplification rule must be used again to deduce D.

        1 (D . E) . P /∴ D
        2 D . E   1,Simp.
        3 D   2,Simp.

The same rule may be applied more than once in a proof, as
the same line may be used more than once.

    Here are more exercises, in which you are required to
construct the proofs for yourself. Try to work backwards
from the conclusion, to see how it can be derived from the
premisses. Remember to look for substitution instances, and
to keep running your eye over the lines you have, to see how
they can be used to derive the conclusion. You may find,
especially at first, that you have to scrap your working and
begin over again. Do not let this dismay you; you can hardly
expect to learn without making some mistakes. Try not
to look at the answers until you have made at least three
attempts to derive the conclusion. None of the proofs in
the exercises requires more than ten lines.

Exercises

Construct formal proofs for the following;

1   (1) (A ⊃ S) . (B ⊃ F)
     (2) A ∨ B
     (3) (S ⊃ B) . (F ⊃ W)   /∴ B ∨ W
2   (1) (R ⊃ P) . (P ⊃ ~L)
     (2) T ⊃ L
     (3) R ∨ T   /∴ P ∨ L
3   (1) (A ∨ G) ⊃ S
     (2) A . T   /∴ S
4   (1) A ∨ ~I
     (2) D ⊃ I
     (3) ~A
     (4) (~D . ~I) ⊃ W   /∴ W
5   (1) S ⊃ P
     (2) C ⊃ ~F
     (3) I ⊃ F
     (4) O ⊃ ~P
     (5) O ∨ C   /∴ ~S ∨ ~I
6   (1) (~K . P) ⊃ (B ∨ R)
     (2) ~K ⊃ (B ⊃ D)
     (3) K ∨ (R ⊃ E)
     (4) ~K . P   /∴ D ∨ E
7   (1) C ⊃ N
     (2) N ⊃ I
     (3) I ⊃ S
     (4) (C ⊃ S) ⊃ (N ⊃ C)
     (5) ~C   /∴ ~N
8   (1) (A ⊃ B) . (B ⊃ ~C)
     (2) C ⊃ ~D
     (3) B ⊃ E
     (4) ~D ⊃ F
     (5) ~E ∨ ~F   /∴ ~A ∨ ~C
9   (1) (G ∨ H) ⊃ ~I
     (2) I ∨ H
     (3) (H ∨ ~G) ⊃ J
     (4) G   /∴ J ∨ ~H
10   (1) (R ⊃ P) . (~P ⊃ H)
     (2) (M ⊃ D) . (D ⊃ R)
     (3) (~M ∨ ~R) ⊃ (~P ∨ ~D)
     (4) ~M   /∴ ~R ∨ ~M

11   (1) A ⊃ B
       (2) C ⊃ D
       (3) ~B ∨ ~D
       (4) ~E
       (5) (~A ∨ ~C) ⊃ (E ∨ F)   /∴ F
12   (1) (A . B) ⊃ [A ⊃ (D . E)]
       (2) (A . B) . C   /∴ D ∨ E

Note: Before you check your solutions, you should read the next section.

5 When you check your completed proofs against ours, you may find that there are differences between them. You need not assume automatically that yours are incorrect, for there is more than one way of constructing a proof. But if your completed proof is different, then check it very carefully.

1 Does your proof contain the same number of lines as ours?
    (a) Perhaps you have used exactly the same rules, but used them in a different order. In this case, have you used them on the same lines, even though these are differently numbered? If so, your proof is satisfactory.
    (b) Have you used different rules? Then make quite sure that you have not misinterpreted or misapplied a rule. If you have derived the conclusion by using different rules, you may still be correct, but please check your working very carefully.
2 Have you taken more lines than we have to complete the proof? Check very carefully, as in 1(b). It is not wrong to use more lines, but it is better to use as few as possible.
3 Have you taken fewer lines to complete your proof than we have? Again, check very carefully as in 1(b). Make quite sure that you have not used two rules together. Check our proof. Have we used any unnecessary lines? If so, where? If you are absolutely sure that you have made no mistakes, then your proof is better than ours. (Economy is a virtue in logic.)

6 *Using logical equivalences.* We have already seen (in chapter 13 of the previous part) that one expression is called *logically equivalent* to another if the two expressions have the same truth-table. Another way of putting this is to say that two expressions are logically equivalent if the biconditional linking them is a tautology. For example: '$p \lor \sim q$' and '$q \supset p$' have the same truth-table:

$$
\begin{array}{cc}
p \lor \sim q & q \supset p \\
1\,1 \;\; 0\,1 & 1\,1 \;\; 1 \\
1\,1 \;\; 1\,0 & 0\,1 \;\; 1 \\
0\,0 \;\; 0\,1 & 1\,0 \;\; 0 \\
0\,1 \;\; 1\,0 & 0\,1 \;\; 0
\end{array}
$$

Each expression has this set of truth values: 1101
and if we join them by the biconditional ($\equiv$), we have:

$$
\begin{array}{cc}
(p \lor \sim q) \equiv (q \supset p) \\
1\,1 \;\; 0\,1 \;\; 1 \quad 1\,1 \;\; 1 \\
1\,1 \;\; 1\,0 \;\; 1 \quad 0\,1 \;\; 1 \\
0\,0 \;\; 0\,1 \;\; 1 \quad 1\,0 \;\; 0 \\
0\,1 \;\; 1\,0 \;\; 1 \quad 0\,1 \;\; 0
\end{array}
$$

in which the main column consists only of ones showing that the whole expression is a logical truth.

We have also seen, throughout our study of the logic of propositions that we are concerned solely with the truth-values of expressions and not with the actual content or linguistic meaning of the expressions themselves. It follows from this that whenever two expressions have the same truth-table, that is, the same truth values in the same order, they are entirely equivalent from the point of view of logic. And just as, for example, in English, the expressions 'my mother's father' and 'my maternal grandfather' mean the same thing so that one or the other may be used indifferently without changing our meaning, so too in logic. We may substitute for any expressions any of its logical equivalents without change of logical meaning. This freedom is extremely useful in constructing proofs, as we shall see.

We shall first of all state a general rule (the Rule of Replacement) which says that: *Any logically equivalent expressions may replace each other wherever they occur*. We shall then list some logical equivalences which are found particularly useful in constructing proofs and which we shall take as rules. As we list these expressions, you should demonstrate, by truth-tables, that they are indeed logically equivalent. So that these new rules can be more easily assimilated, we will give five of them first and follow them with some examples for practice.

10 *Commutation* (Com.): $(p \vee q) \equiv (q \vee p)$
$(p \cdot q) \equiv (q \cdot p)$

This rule permits the substitution of $q \vee p$ for $p \vee q$ and vice versa, wherever they occur, and it also permits the substitution of $q \cdot p$ for $p \cdot q$ wherever these expressions occur. Please note that the commutation rule applies only to those expressions connected by the vel sign, or to those connected by the dot sign. It does *not* apply to the hook sign. You will see why not if you compare the truth-tables of '$p \supset q$' and '$q \supset p$'. The first is 1011 and the second is 1101.

11 *Association* (Assoc.): $[p \vee (q \vee r)] \equiv [(p \vee q) \vee r]$
$[p \cdot (q \cdot r)] \equiv [(p \cdot q) \cdot r]$

This rule, as you can see, allows us to change the position of the brackets. An expression which consists of the two expressions p, and $(q \vee r)$ connected by the vel sign, may be replaced by one which consists of the two expressions $(p \vee q)$ and r, connected by the vel sign. The rule applies similarly to conjunctions. But please note carefully that:

(a) It applies only to those expressions in which all of the connectives are either $\vee$, or to those on which all of the connectives are ..
(b) It does not apply to those expressions which contain both vel signs and dot signs.
(c) It does not apply to expressions connected by the hook sign.

12 *Distribution* (Dist.): $[p \cdot (q \lor r)] \equiv [(p \cdot q) \lor (p \cdot r)]$
$[p \lor (q \cdot r)] \equiv [(p \lor q) \cdot (p \lor r)]$

This rule does apply to expressions which contain both vel signs and dot signs. You should make quite sure that you see the difference between this rule and the association rule.

13 De Morgan's Theorems (de M.):

$$\sim(p \cdot q) \equiv (\sim p \lor \sim q)$$
$$\sim(p \lor q) \equiv (\sim p \cdot \sim q)$$

This rule enables us to alter the scope of a negation sign and so to substitute an expression that does not contain brackets for one which does; and vice versa. (Notice that this rule does not apply to the hook sign.)

14 Double Negation (D.N.): $p \equiv \sim\sim p$

There is one *very important difference* between the use of the first nine rules of inference (given on p. 105) and the use of those which permit the substitution of logically equivalent expressions. The first nine rules may be used only when *entire lines of a proof* are substitution instances of the rule in question. For example, suppose that 'P ⊃ Q' is a whole line in a proof. We may use the Addition Rule

$$p$$
$$\therefore p \lor q$$

to substitute the line 'P ⊃ Q' by '(P ⊃ Q) $\lor$ R'. We could *not* use the rule *within the line* to substitute 'P ⊃ Q' by '(P $\lor$ R) ⊃ Q'. But those rules of inference which are instances of the Rule of Replacement may be used to replace expressions by their logical equivalents *wherever they occur*. They may be used on whole lines or on parts of lines.

Here are some examples of proofs in which logically equivalent expressions have been substituted for one another.

Commutation (Com.) $(p \lor q) \equiv (q \lor p)$
$(p \cdot q) \equiv (q \cdot p)$

You will appreciate the inclusion of this rule if you consider the disjunctive syllogism rule, which you have already used. According to this rule, given $p \lor q$, and $\sim p$, we may infer q. But the rule does not permit the inference of p, given $p \lor q$ and $\sim q$. If we wish to prove:

> 1 $(A \supset B) \lor (C \cdot D)$
> 2 $\sim(C \cdot D)$ $/\therefore A \supset B$

we cannot use the DS rule to deduce $A \supset B$. But we can, in accordance with the commutation rule, change the position of the two disjuncts in line 1, and then use DS:

> 1 $(A \supset B) \lor (C \cdot D)$
> 2 $\sim(C \cdot D)$ $/\therefore A \supset B$
> 3 $(C \cdot D) \lor (A \supset B)$ 1,Comm.
> 4 $A \supset B$ 3,2,DS

Suppose we had the following example:

> 1 $(A \cdot B) \supset (C \lor D)$
> 2 $B \cdot A$ $/\therefore C \lor D$

We cannot use the *Modus ponens* rule forthwith, for line 2 does not affirm the antecedent of line 1. But we may, by using the commutation rule, change the position of the conjuncts in line 1, or in line 2.

> 1 $(A \cdot B) \supset (C \lor D)$
> 2 $B \cdot A$ $/\therefore C \lor D$
> 3 $(B \cdot A) \supset (C \lor D)$ 1,Comm.
> 4 $C \lor D$ 3,2,MP

Association (Assoc.) $[p \lor (q \lor r)] \equiv [(p \lor q) \lor r]$
$ [p \cdot (q \cdot r)] \equiv [(p \cdot q) \cdot r]$

Suppose we have as lines in a proof:

> 1 $K \lor (N \lor M)$
> 2 $\sim(K \lor N)$

and we wish to deduce M.

The association rule permits us to substitute for line 1, the logically equivalent expression (K ∨ N) ∨ M. We write this as the third line, and we may then derive M by DS.

Suppose we wish to derive R from the line T . (U . R)

$$1 \quad T . (U . R) \quad /\therefore R$$

The simplification rule alone will not permit us to do this. We use the association rule to replace line 1 by the logically equivalent expression (T . U) . R (line 2). We then replace line 2 by the logically equivalent expression R . (T . U) according to the commutation rule (line 3). Finally, we complete the proof by using the simplification rule (line 4).

```
1  T . (U . R)    /∴ R
2  (T . U) . R    1,Assn.
3  R . (T . U)    2,Comm.
4  R              3,Simp.
```

Distribution (Dist.) $[p . (q \lor r)] \equiv [(p . q) \lor (p . r)]$
$\qquad\qquad\qquad\quad [p \lor (q . r)] \equiv [(p \lor q) . (p \lor r)]$

The distribution rule can be used as in the following example:

```
1  W . (X ∨ Y)
2  ∼(W . X)           /∴ W . Y
3  (W . X) ∨ (W . Y)  1,Dist.
4  (W . Y)            3,2,DS
```

Here is another example in which the distribution rule has been used. But here we have first used the commutation rule as *part* of a line: as part of line 1.

```
1  (P ∨ W) . (W ∨ K)
2  ∼W                  /∴ P . K
3  (W ∨ P) . (W ∨ K)  1,Comm.
4  W ∨ (P . K)        3,Dist.
5  P . K              4,2,DS
```

De Morgan Theorems (de M) $\sim(p . q) \equiv (\sim p \lor \sim q)$
$\qquad\qquad\qquad\qquad\quad \sim(p \lor q) \equiv (\sim p . \sim q)$

This rule enables us to replace a negated conjunction by the disjunction of two negated expressions, and vice versa. And it enables us to replace a negated disjunction by the conjunction of two negated expressions, and vice versa. The rule has been used in the following example:

```
1  ~(P ∨ Q) . R      /∴ ~P
2  (~P . ~Q) . R      1,de M.
3  ~P . ~Q            2,Simp.
4  ~P                 3,Simp.
```

This rule is very useful used in conjunction with the addition rule. Suppose we have the following:

```
1  M ⊃ (N . O)
2  ~N                 /∴ ~M
```

If we had ~(N . O) as a line in the proof, we could deduce ~M directly by the *Modus tollens* rule. But we do not have this as a line. ~(N . O) is equivalent to ~N ∨ ~O, and we can add ~O to ~N on line 2, in accordance with the addition rule.

```
1  M ⊃ (N . O)
2  ~N                 /∴ ~M
3  ~N ∨ ~O            2,Add.
4  ~(N . O)           3,de M.
5  ~M                 1,4,MT
```

Do not forget the extremely useful addition rule, which allows the addition of any expression whatsoever. If you are at all doubtful about this, then demonstrate, by using truth-tables that (~N ∨ ~O) is logically implied by ~N, that is, that ~N ⊃ (~N ∨ ~O) is a logical truth. Or, demonstrate by using truth-tables that to any expression whatsoever, we may add any expression whatsoever; for example:

```
1  P
2  P ∨ [L . M) ⊃ (M ⊃ L)]
```

Write this as a material implication:

$$P ⊃ \{P ∨ [(L . M) ⊃ (M ⊃ L)]\}$$

and demonstrate by using shorter truth-tables that it is a logical truth.

Double Negation (DN) $p \equiv \sim\sim p$

Suppose we wish to apply the de Morgan rules to the expression: $\sim(\sim p \vee \sim q)$. In applying the de Morgan rules, we bring the negation sign from outside the bracket, negate each component, and change the sign, from disjunction to conjunction. This will give us:

$$\sim\sim p \vee \sim\sim q$$

The double negation rule permits us to write:

$$p \cdot q \text{ for } \sim\sim p \cdot \sim\sim q$$

The secrets of being able to construct a formal proof are, as we have said before, to try to see how the conclusion can be derived from the premisses, using the given rules of inference, and to look for substitution instances. Now you have five more rules at your disposal which allow you to substitute logically equivalent expressions where this will help the deduction of the conclusion. It is also useful to jot down on a bit of scrap paper the expressions which are equivalent to the conclusion. This may help you to see how the conclusion can be derived. To develop a facility in constructing proofs, you need to be able to use the rules and to see where a substitution would be helpful. This takes practice, and so before we give you the remaining rules, here are some exercises. Use any of the rules we have given so far.

Exercises

Prove the validity of the following abbreviated arguments:

1   (1) $\sim E \vee F$
    (2) E $/ \therefore$ F   (2 rules)
2   (1) $\sim C \vee \sim D$ $/ \therefore \sim(C \cdot D)$ (1 rule)
3   (1) $\sim(C \vee D)$ $/ \therefore \sim C \cdot \sim D$
                                                             (1 rule)
4   (1) $R \vee (U \cdot W)$ $/ \therefore R \vee W$ (3 rules)

5   (1) $(A \lor B) . (A \lor C)$
     (2) $\sim A$ /∴ B . C   (2 rules)

6   (1) $A \lor (B \lor C)$ /∴ $(A \lor B) \lor C$
                                           (1 rule)

7   (1) $A \lor (B \lor C)$ /∴ $C \lor (A \lor B)$
                                          (2 rules)

8   (1) $A \lor (B \lor C)$
     (2) $\sim C$ /∴ A ∨ B   (3 rules)

9   (1) $(X \lor N) \supset (Y . P)$
     (2) $N \lor X$ /∴ Y . P   (2 rules)

10 (1) $(X \lor N) \supset (Y . P)$
     (2) $N \lor X$ /∴ Y   (3 rules)

11 (1) $(X \lor N) \supset (Y . P)$
     (2) $N \lor X$ /∴ P

12 (1) $N \lor (M \lor V)$
     (2) $\sim (M \lor V)$ /∴ N

13 (1) $[(F \lor G) . (H \supset I)] . (J . K)$ /∴ J . K

14 (1) $[(F \lor G) . (H \supset I)] . (J . K)$ /∴ K

15 (1) $[(F \lor G) . (H \supset I)] . (J . K)$ /∴ J ∨ N

16 (1) $K . (L \lor W)$
     (2) $\sim (K . L)$ /∴ K . W

17 (1) $(P . Q) \lor (P . R)$ /∴ P

18 (1) $(Z \lor Y) . (Z \lor K)$
     (2) $\sim (Y . K)$ /∴ Z

19 (1) $\sim (\sim E \lor \sim G)$ /∴ E

20 (1) $\sim (\sim H \lor \sim I)$ /∴ I

21 (1) $H \supset (K . L)$
     (2) $\sim K$ /∴ ∼H

22 (1) $\sim (V \lor W) . R$ /∴ R

23 (1) $\sim (V \lor W) . R$ /∴ ∼V

24 (1) $(P \supset Q) . (R \supset T)$
     (2) $\sim T$ /∴ ∼R

25 (1) $(P \lor Q) \lor [(R \lor S) . (T \lor U)]$
     (2) $\sim P$
     (3) $\sim Q$ /∴ R ∨ S

The remaining rules of inference

Now we give you some more logically equivalent expressions which can be used as rules of inference.

    15   *Transposition* (Trans.) $(p \supset q) \equiv (\sim q \supset \sim p)$

We have said above that $p \supset q$ is not logically equivalent to $q \supset p$, and we hope you demonstrated this for yourself. $p \supset q$ is logically equivalent to $\sim q \supset \sim p$. Consider a statement having the form $p \supset q$.

> If it rains then the pavements are wet

This is *not* logically equivalent to:

> If the pavements are wet then it is raining

The first statement may be true and the second false: the pavements may have been washed.

> If it is raining, then the pavements are wet

is logically equivalent to:

> If the pavements are not wet, then it is not raining.

You should continue to use truth-tables to confirm these logical equivalences, and not just rely on your intuitive understanding. $\sim p \supset \sim q$ is logically equivalent (by Transposition) to $\sim\sim q \supset \sim\sim p$, which, by Double Negation is logically equivalent to $q \supset p$.

16 *Definition of Material Implication* (Mat.Imp.)

$$(p \supset q) \equiv (\sim p \lor q)$$

These two expressions have the same truth values:

$(\sim p \supset q) \equiv (\sim\sim p \lor q)$ by Mat.Imp.; and
$(\sim\sim p \lor q) \equiv (p \lor q)$ by Double Negation.

Had this rule been at your disposal when you did the exercises on p. 111 you could have completed proof No. 8, using far fewer lines:

1	$(A \supset B) . (B \supset \sim C)$	
2	$C \supset \sim D$	
3	$B \supset E$	
4	$\sim D \supset F$	
5	$\sim E \lor \sim F$	$/\therefore \sim A \lor \sim C$
6	$A \supset \sim C$	1,HS
7	$\sim A \lor \sim C$	6,Mat.Imp.

By using the Material Implication rule, the proof takes seven lines, instead of ten. We have used only the first two premisses, but there is no rule which says that we must use *all* the premisses.

Here is an example in which we have used both the Transposition rule and the Material Implication rule:

$$
\begin{array}{lll}
1 & K \supset L & \\
2 & \sim K \supset N & /\therefore L \lor N \\
3 & \sim L \supset \sim K & 1,\text{Trans.} \\
4 & \sim L \supset N & 3,2,\text{HS} \\
5 & \sim\sim L \lor N & 4,\text{Mat.Imp.} \\
6 & L \lor N & 5,\text{DN}
\end{array}
$$

17 *Definition of Material Equivalence* (Mat.Equiv.)

$$(p \equiv q) \equiv [(p \supset q) \cdot (q \supset p)]$$
$$(p \equiv q) \equiv [(p \cdot q) \lor (\sim p \cdot \sim q)]$$

We have already, in effect, given you the first of these equivalences on p. 72 when we introduced the symbol for Material Equivalence. Now we give you another expression which is logcally equivalent to $p \equiv q$. This rule is used in the following example:

$$
\begin{array}{lll}
1 & (F \equiv G) \supset (H \lor I) & \\
2 & F \cdot G & /\therefore H \lor I \\
3 & (F \cdot G) \lor (\sim F \cdot \sim G) & 2,\text{Add.} \\
4 & F \equiv G & 3,\text{Mat.Equiv.} \\
5 & H \lor I & 1,4,\text{MP}
\end{array}
$$

18 *Tautology* (Taut.) $p \equiv p \lor p$
$$p \equiv p \cdot p$$

This rule has been used in the following example:

$$
\begin{array}{lll}
1 & \sim B \supset C & \\
2 & C \supset B & /\therefore B \\
3 & \sim B \supset B & 1,2,\text{HS} \\
4 & \sim\sim B \lor B & 3,\text{Mat.Imp.} \\
5 & B \lor B & 4,\text{DN} \\
6 & B & 5,\text{Taut.}
\end{array}
$$

19   *Exportation* (Exp.) $[(p \cdot q) \supset r] \equiv [p \supset (q \supset r)]$

Here is an example of the use of this rule:

> 1   (A . E) ⊃ F
> 2   (E ⊃ F) ⊃ G
> 3   A   /∴ G
> 4   A ⊃ (E ⊃ F)   1,Exp.
> 5   A ⊃ G   4,2HS
> 6   G   5,3MP

Below we give you some exercises which will enable you to become familiar with these rules.

Exercises

(A)
   1   (1) ~A ∨ B   /∴ A ⊃ B   (1 rule)
   2   (1) ~H ⊃ ~I
       (2) I   /∴ H   (2 rules)
   3   (1) S ≡ P   /∴ (S ⊃ P) . (P ⊃ S)
                                               (1 rule)
   4   (1) S ≡ P   /∴ P ⊃ S   (3 rules)
   5   (1) P . Q   /∴ P ≡ Q   (2 rules)
   6   (1) R ⊃ J   /∴ ~J ⊃ ~R   (1 rule)
   7   (1) ~L ⊃ ~M   /∴ ~M ∨ L   (2 rules)
   8   (1) (P ⊃ Q) . (R ⊃ Q)
       (2) P ∨ R   /∴ Q   (2 rules)
   9   (1) (C . D) ⊃ J   /∴ C ⊃ (D ⊃ J)   (1 rule)
  10   (1) (F . G) ⊃ J
       (2) (G ⊃ J) ⊃ C   /∴ F ⊃ C   (2 rules)

(B)   The following exercises will give you practice in applying all nineteen rules of inference.

   1   (1) (S . U) ⊃ P
       (2) (U ⊃ P) ⊃ W
       (3) S   /∴ W
   2   (1) A ∨ (B . C)
       (2) (A ∨ B) ⊃ D   /∴ C ∨ D
   3   (1) G ⊃ (B ⊃ C)
       (2) G . ~C   /∴ ~B
   4   (1) P ⊃ S   /∴ P ⊃ (H ⊃ S)

  5 (1) (F ⊃ R) . (L ⊃ U)
      (2) (R . U) ⊃ C
      (3) ~C   /∴ ~F ∨ ~L

  6 (1) (~A ∨ B) . (A ⊃ C)
      (2) B ⊃ (C ⊃ E)   /∴ A ⊃ E

  7 (1) B
      (2) (C . B) ⊃ ~M
      (3) M   /∴ ~C

  8 (1) (A ⊃ B) . (C ⊃ B)
      (2) D ⊃ (A ∨ C)
      (3) D   /∴ B

  9 (1) ~K ∨ L
      (2) ~M ⊃ ~L   /∴ K ⊃ M

10 (1) (A . B) ⊃ (C ∨ D)
      (2) D ⊃ E
      (3) E ⊃ F
      (4) ~(F . G)
      (5) ~G . ~C   /∴ A ⊃ ~B

11 (1) G ⊃ (S ⊃ U)
      (2) G . ~U   /∴ ~S

12 (1) (C ⊃ E) . (P ⊃ L)
      (2) (L . E) ⊃ S
      (3) ~S   /∴ ~C ∨ ~P

13 (1) [(A . B) ⊃ C] . [(A . ~B) ⊃ ~C]
                      /∴ A ⊃ (B ≡ C)

14 (1) (J . S) ⊃ W
      (2) W ⊃ T
      (3) ~T . J   /∴ ~S

15 (1) H ⊃ ~E
      (2) ~S . E
      (3) E ⊃ (D ∨ S)   /∴ D ∨ H

16 (1) A ⊃ (F . ~G)
      (2) (~G ∨ R) ⊃ ~P
      (3) P . ~Q   /∴ ~A

17 (1) (P ∨ Q) . (P ∨ R)
      (2) P ⊃ S
      (3) S ⊃ T
      (4) (Q . R) ⊃ (U ⊃ T)
      (5) ~T   /∴ ~U

18 (1) B ∨ T
      (2) (B ∨ C) ⊃ (L . M)
      (3) ~L   /∴ T

19 (1) (P . Q) ∨ (R . S)
  (2) P ⊃ ∼P   /∴ S
20 (1) (P ∨ S) ⊃ (I . C)
  (2) I ⊃ N
  (3) ∼N   /∴ ∼P
21 (1) (J ∨ S) ⊃ (C . V) /∴ ∼J ∨ C
22 (1) (R ⊃ W) . (P ⊃ M)
  (2) R ∨ P
  (3) (R ⊃ ∼M) . (P ⊃ ∼W)
        /∴ M ≡ ∼W
23 (1) D ∨ (R . F)
  (2) D ⊃ F   /∴F
24 (1) W ⊃ M
  (2) M ⊃ ∼(L . G)
  (3) (∼L ⊃ D) . ∼D
  (4) G   /∴ ∼W
25 (1) (S ⊃ A) . (A ⊃ ∼R)
  (2) V ⊃ B
  (3) B ⊃ ∼R
  (4) R ∨ F
  (5) S ∨ V   /∴ F

7 Conditional proof

We shall look at two further methods for helping us to prove
conclusions from premises. The first of these is known as
the *Method of Conditional Proof*. We have seen that every
valid argument can be expressed as a conditional statement
whose antecedent is the premises of the argument and
whose consequent is the conclusion. Let us confine our
attention, for the time being, to arguments which have
conditional statements as their conclusion. Consider, for
example:

  1 A ⊃ (B ∨ C)
  2 C ⊃ D
  3 ∼B   /∴ A ⊃ C

This has three premises and a conclusion: A ⊃ C. Let us
suppose that the three premises are conjoined (as they would

be if we were constructing a truth-table) and call the conjunction Z. That is to say we are supposing that:

$$[A \supset (B \lor C) . (C \supset D)] . \sim B$$

is abbreviated to: Z. Then the argument has the form:

$$Z \supset (A \supset C)$$

Now we know, by the Exportation Rule (p. 123 above) that this is logically equivalent to:

$$(Z . A) \supset C$$

What we have done is this. (1) We have taken the antecedent of the conclusion and added it to the premisses as an additional premiss. (2) By this means we prove the consequent of the conclusion. (3) Since $(Z . A) \supset C$ is logically equivalent to $Z \supset (A \supset C)$ we have proved what we were originally asked to do, namely, that $(A \supset C)$ follows from the premisses.

The conditional proof is as follows:

1	$A \supset (B \lor C)$	
2	$C \supset D$	
3	$\sim B$	$/ \therefore A \supset C$
4	A	$/ \therefore C$ (Conditional Proof, or CP for short)
5	$B \lor C$	1,4,MP
6	C	3,5,DS
7	$A \supset C$	4–6,CP

This proof is considerably shorter than it would have been, had we not used Conditional Proof. If fact, the use of this method does often shorten proofs. But do not assume that it is always a short cut. Just make use of it when you find that it helps in constructing your proof. The method can also be used to carry out proofs which cannot be done by the means that you have learned so far. (See, for example, (3) of the exercises that follow.)

Exercises

In doing the following exercises, use conditional proof only for 1, 2, 3, and 5. For the rest, construct proofs first by using the nineteen rules of inference and then by conditional proof.

1 (1) A ⊃ (B . C)
   (2) (B ∨ C) ⊃ I   /∴ A ⊃ I
2 (1) A ⊃ (B ∨ C)
   (2) B ⊃ C   /∴ A ⊃ C
3 (1) P ⊃ Q   /∴ P ⊃ ~ (P ⊃ ~Q)
4 (1) D ⊃ (F ∨ T)
   (2) ~F   /∴ ~T ⊃ (~D ∨ S)
5 (1) (E . S) ⊃ P
   (2) (E . ~S) ⊃ ~P   /∴ E ⊃ [(S . P) ∨ (~S . ~P)]
6 (1) A . B
   (2) (A ∨ B) ⊃ F
   (3) F ⊃ (C ⊃ D)
   (4) D ⊃ E   /∴ C ⊃ E
7 (1) P ⊃ (Q ⊃ ~P)
   (2) P ⊃ Q
   (3) ~P ⊃ ~Q   /∴ P ⊃ (P . Q)
8 (1) (A ∨ B) ⊃ (C . D) /∴ A ⊃ C
9 (1) (A ∨ B) ⊃ (C . D)
   (2) B   /∴ ~D ⊃ A
10 (1) (Q . R) ⊃ S
   (2) (R ⊃ S) ⊃ T   /∴ Q ⊃ T

8 Indirect proof

This is a very ancient method of proof which first appears in the writings of the Greek mathematicians in the fourth century BC. In traditional editions of Euclid's geometry it is referred to as *reductio ad absurdum*. This, you will remember, is one of the ways of referring to the shorter truth-table method where we assume the contradictory of what we are trying to prove in order to show that a particular argument form is valid. The method of indirect proof uses the same device. We add to our premises the *negation* of the conclusion to be proved. If, as a result of this additional premiss, we can prove a contradiction, we know that the conclusion does in fact follow from the premises without the addition of any further premiss.

Let us look at an example:

```
1  (A . B) ⊃ C
2  (B ⊃ C) ⊃ D
3  A              /∴ D
4  ~D             (Indirect Proof, or IP, for short)
5  A ⊃ (B ⊃ C)    1,Exp.
6  (B ⊃ C)        3,5,MP
7  ~(B ⊃ C)       2,4,MT
```

We have now proved two contradictory propositions, 6 and 7. We do not need to go any further although we can now prove our original conclusion without any trouble. For *any proposition at all* follows from a contradiction. Suppose that we have two contradictory premises: P and ~P. We proceed as follows:

```
1  P
2  ~P     /∴ Q (where Q is any proposition at all)
3  P ∨ Q  1,Add.
4  Q      2,3,DS
```

You may find that some arguments yield conclusions which seem extraordinary even though they come out as valid when tested. This will usually be because there is a contradiction hidden in the implications of the premises. (See, for example, (17) of Exercises B at the end of Part I.)

Like conditional proof, indirect proof often yields shorter proofs than the rules of inference by themselves. Here is an example:

```
1  A ∨ (B . C)
2  A ⊃ C    /∴ C
3  ~C       IP
4  ~A       2,3,MT
5  B . C    1,4,DS
6  C . B    5,Comm.
7  C        6,Simp.
8  C . ~C   7,3,Conj.
```

Compare this with a formal proof of the same example.

1	A ∨ (B . C)	
2	A ⊃ C	/∴ C
3	(A ∨ B) . (A ∨ C)	1,Dist.
4	(A ∨ C) . (A ∨ B)	3,Comm.
5	A ∨ C	4,Simp.
6	C ∨ A	5,Comm.
7	~~C ∨ A	6,DN
8	~C ⊃ A	7,Mat.Imp.
9	~C ⊃ C	8,2,HS
10	~~C ∨ C	9,Mat.Imp.
11	C ∨ C	10,DN
12	C	11,Taut.

As you see, the indirect proof is shorter, and you may be able to see more easily how to proceed with the deduction if you assume ~C.

All that is necessary in an indirect proof is that a contradiction be deduced. *Any* contradiction will do.

Exercises

Prove the conclusions by the Method of Indirect Proof:

1   (1) (D ∨ E) ⊃ (F ⊃ G)
      (2) (~G ∨ H) ⊃ (D . F)   /∴ G
2   (1) (H ⊃ I) . (J ⊃ K)
      (2) (I ∨ K) ⊃ L
      (3) ~L   /∴ ~(H ∨ J)
3   (1) (V ⊃ ~W) . (X ⊃ Y)
      (2) (~W ⊃ Z) . (Y ⊃ ~A)
      (3) (Z ⊃ ~B) . (~A ⊃ C)
      (4) V . X   /∴ ~B . C
4   (1) P
      (2) (~P ∨ ~S) ⊃ (~P . ~R)   /∴ S
5   (1) A ⊃ (F . ~G)
      (2) (~G ∨ R) ⊃ ~P
      (3) P . Q   /∴ ~A
6   (1) B ∨ T
      (2) (B ∨ C) ⊃ (L . M)
      (3) ~L   /∴ T

7   (1) A ⊃ (F . ~G)
    (2) (~G ∨ R) ⊃ ~P
    (3) P . ~Q   /∴ ~A
8   (1) A ⊃ B
    (2) ~A ⊃ C   /∴ B ∨ C
9   (1) W ⊃ M
    (2) M ⊃ ~E
    (3) ~(E ⊃ F)   /∴ ~W
10 (1) (A . B) ⊃ (C ∨ D)
    (2) D ⊃ E
    (3) E ⊃ F
    (4) ~(F . G)
    (5) G . ~C   /∴ A ⊃ ~B

Exercises on Part II

(A)   Turn back to the arguments at **B** of the Exercises on Part I
      (p. 99) and construct formal proofs for those that you have
      already shown to be valid. (Use any method that you find
      convenient.)

(B)   Construct formal proofs for the following:

1   (1) ~H ∨ R
    (2) H   /∴ R
2   (1) H ∨ B
    (2) ~B   /∴ H
3   (1) ~(M ∨ V)   /∴ ~M
4   (1) S ⊃ L   /∴ S ⊃ (L ∨ W)
5   (1) M ⊃ C
    (2) C ⊃ F
    (3) ~F   /∴ ~M
6   (1) W ∨ D
    (2) W ⊃ F
    (3) ~F   /∴ D
7   (1) B ⊃ D
    (2) (B ⊃ D) ∨ ~A   /∴ (A . B) ⊃ D
8   (1) (D . P) ⊃ B
    (2) (P ⊃ B) ⊃ C
    (3) D   /∴ C
9   (1) G ⊃ (S ⊃ U)
    (2) G . ~U   /∴ ~S

10   (1) $(C \supset E) . (P \supset L)$
     (2) $(L . E) \supset S$
     (3) $\sim S$ $/ \therefore \sim C \vee \sim P$
11   (1) $P \supset (Q . R)$
     (2) $(Q . R) \supset S$
     (3) $\sim S$ $/ \therefore P \supset Q$
12   (1) $F \supset G$
     (2) $G \supset \sim K$
     (3) $\sim K \supset M$
     (4) $F . L$ $/ \therefore M \vee L$
13   (1) $(P \supset Q) \supset R$
     (2) $(S \supset T) \supset U$
     (3) $P \supset Q$ $/ \therefore R \vee U$
14   (1) $P \supset (S . R)$
     (2) $Q \supset \sim(S . R)$
     (3) Q $/ \therefore P \supset T$
15   (1) $D \supset (F \vee T)$
     (2) $\sim F$ $/ \therefore (D . \sim S) \supset T$
16   (This example should be done without using Indirect Proof.)
     (1) $A \vee B$
     (2) $(A \vee C) \supset (D . E)$
     (3) $\sim D$ $/ \therefore B . \sim C$
17   (1) $(A \vee B) \supset (C . D)$
     (2) $\sim C$ $/ \therefore \sim B$
18   (1) $A \supset B$
     (2) $B \supset \sim(C . D)$
     (3) $(\sim C \supset E) . \sim E$
     (4) D $/ \therefore \sim A$
19   (1) $(P . Q) \supset R$
     (2) $(P \supset R) \supset S$
     (3) $\sim Q \vee T$ $/ \therefore Q \supset (S . T)$
20   (1) $(D \supset \sim P) . (P \supset Q)$
     (2) $Q \supset D$
     (3) $\sim R \supset P$ $/ \therefore R$
21   (1) $S \supset (T \supset U)$
     (2) $U \supset \sim U$
     (3) $(V \supset S) . (W \supset T)$ $/ \therefore V \supset \sim W$
22   (1) $X \supset (Y \supset Z)$
     (2) $X \supset (A \supset B)$
     (3) $X . (Y \vee A)$
     (4) $\sim Z$ $/ \therefore B$

23 (1) C ⊃ (D ⊃ ~C)
    (2) C ≡ D   /∴ ~C . ~D
24 (1) E . (F ∨ G)
    (2) (E . G) ⊃ ~(H ∨ I)
    (3) (~H ∨ ~I) ⊃ ~(E . F)
                 /∴ H ≡ I
25 (1) (A ⊃ S) . (B ⊃ F)
    (2) A ∨ B
    (3) (S ⊃ B) . (F ⊃ W)
    (4) ~(A ∨ G)   /∴ W
26 (1) P ⊃ (Q ∨ R)
    (2) S ⊃ ~Q
    (3) (T ∨ U) ⊃ ~R
    (4) ~(S ⊃ ~T)   /∴ ~P
27 (1) (A . B) ⊃ (C ⊃ D)
    (2) ~E ⊃ ~D
    (3) ~(F ∨ G)
    (4) E ⊃ F   /∴ (B . C) ⊃ ~A
28 (1) A ⊃ (~B ⊃ C)
    (2) C ⊃ (A ⊃ D)
    (3) B ⊃ F
    (4) ~(A ⊃ F)
    (5) ~B   /∴ D
29 (1) F ⊃ G
    (2) H ⊃ J
    (3) K ⊃ (H ∨ M)
    (4) ~(L ⊃ G)
    (5) ~J ⊃ F   /∴ ~K
    (6) ~M
30 (1) F ⊃ B
    (2) ~(H ⊃ ~G)
    (3) G ⊃ F
    (4) (~A ⊃ B) ⊃ (C . D)
    (5) ~J ⊃ ~B   /∴ ~A ⊃ J
31 (1) P ⊃ Q   /∴ (P ⊃ ~Q) ⊃ ~P
32 (1) (P ∨ ~Q) ⊃ R
    (2) S ⊃ (T ⊃ ~R)
    (3) ~(S ⊃ ~T)   /∴ P ⊃ T
33 (1) A ⊃ (B . C)
    (2) C ⊃ (~D ∨ ~E)
    (3) ~D ⊃ (E ⊃ F)
    (4) ~E ⊃ ~B   /∴ A ⊃ F

34   (1) (P ⊃ Q) ⊃ R   /∴ P ⊃ (Q ⊃ R)
35   (1) P ∨ Q   /∴ ∼Q ⊃ [∼R ⊃ (∼P ⊃ S)]

(C) Construct formal proofs for the following:

1   If the Foreign Minister is an agent of the CIA the
    government's foreign policy can be understood. If the
    Minister for Industry is an agent of the KGB the
    government's industrial policy can be understood.
    Either the Prime Minister is being blackmailed or he
    has some control over his cabinet. If the Prime Minister
    has some control over his cabinet, then it is false that
    either the government's foreign policy or its industrial
    policy can be understood. The Prime Minister is not
    being blackmailed. *So:* the Foreign Minister is not an
    agent of the CIA.

2   If the Special Branch know about the Home Secretary's
    private life or the newspapers get the story, he will have
    to resign. If the Prime Minister allows the newspapers
    to publish the story, the government will fall. If the
    newspapers get the story, the Prime Minister will not
    allow them to publish it. If the government does not
    fall, the Home Secretary will not have to resign. It is
    false that if the Special Branch know about the Home
    Secretary's private life, the newspapers will get the
    story. *Therefore:* the government will fall.

3   If Mr X gets a knighthood, there will be a scandal. If
    Mr X has made a fortune for the Prime Minister on the
    stock exchange, he will get a knighthood. If Mr X is
    known to control the Downing Street heroin ring, then
    he won't get a knighthood. Mr X will get a knighthood.
    Therefore: If Mr X has not made a fortune for the
    Prime Minister on the Stock Exchange, he is not known
    to control the Downing Street heroin ring.

4   If the Post Office is run by the Mafia, the expense is
    understandable but the inefficiency is not. If it is run
    by the Mafia, then it is not a nationalised industry. If it
    is a nationalised industry, the inefficiency is understand-
    able. It is a nationalised industry. *Therefore:* If the
    inefficiency is not understandable, neither is the ex-
    pense.

5   If the Foundation for Educational Decline reports
    favourably or the Labour Party win the election then

the educational system will deteriorate further and false views on intelligence will receive official backing. If the educational system deteriorates further, then national standards of scientific achievement will sink to those of a banana republic. National standards of scientific achievement will not sink to those of a banana republic. *Therefore:* The Foundation for Educational Decline will not report favourably.

6 If the head of the Race Relations Board is white, the *Guardian* will be displeased. If the head of the Race Relations Board is coloured, the *Telegraph* will be displeased. If the *Guardian* is displeased then the BBC will arrange a protest programme and there will be unrest in Hampstead. If the *Telegraph* is displeased, then there will be questions in the House and unrest in Cheltenham. There will not be questions in the House. *Therefore:* The head of the Race Relations Board won't be coloured.

7 If the Foundation for Educational Decline is a creature of the government, and its findings are despised by serious psychologists, then its advice will carry no authority. If its advice does carry authority, then the comprehensive system of education will continue. If the comprehensive system of education continues, the drop in standards will accelerate, and further evidence will be faked by the Foundation for Educational Decline. If further evidence is faked, then the findings of the Foundation will be despised by serious psychologists. The advice of the Foundation will carry authority. *Therefore:* The Foundation for Educational Decline is not a creature of the government.

8 If, if the head of the Drug Squad is bribed, the Downing Street heroin ring is safe, then addiction will increase. Either the Prime Minister knows about the Downing Street heroin ring or it is false that if the Home Secretary has squared the head of the Drug Squad, the rank and file will want their cut. Addiction won't increase. If the Home Secretary has organised the Downing Street heroin ring, then if he has squared the head of the Drug Squad, the rank and file will want their cut. Either, if the head of the Drug Squad is bribed, the Downing Street heroin ring is safe or the Prime Minister doesn't

know about the Downing Street heroin ring. *Therefore:*
The Home Secretary has not organised the Downing
Street heroin ring.

9 The profession of psychoanalyst is an honourable one
if and only if either Freudian theory is genuinely scientific or psychoanalysts believe it to be so. If Freudian
theory is genuinely scientific then the standard tests
for scientific acceptability are worthless. If the standard
tests for scientific acceptability are not worthless then
Freudian theory is a mere superstition. If Freudian
theory is genuinely scientific then psychoanalytic
treatment produces a statistically significant proportion
of cures. If psychoanalysts believe Freudian theory
to be scientific then the standard tests for scientific
acceptability are worthless. It is false either that psychoanalytic treatment produces a statistically significant
proportion of cures or that the standard tests for
scientific acceptability are worthless. *Therefore:* The
profession of psychoanalyst is not an honourable one.

10 If either the press rumours are true or Tiggy Broms-
grove's diaries can be relied on, then, if the Downing
Street heroin ring is run by Scotland Yard, the Whitehall call girl service is organised from the House of
Lords. If either the Whitehall call girl service is not
organised from the House of Lords or the Archbishop
of Canterbury has called for an enquiry, then the press
rumours are true and the Downing Street heroin ring
is run by Scotland Yard. *Therefore:* the Whitehall call
girl service is organised from the House of Lords.

Part III

The Logic of Predicates (1)

1 In the remaining part of this book, we shall deal with a kind of argument for which the techniques of propositional logic are inadequate. To deal with these arguments, we shall have to go beyond propositional logic. This does not mean that we can forget anything that we have done so far, but it does mean that we shall need to introduce some new notions and some new symbols.

Here are four arguments of the kind we shall consider:

1   Some ratepayers are voters.
    All voters are citizens.
    Therefore: Some citizens are ratepayers.
2   No Quakers are vice traffickers.
    All drug pedlars are vice traffickers.
    Therefore: No drug pedlars are Quakers.
3   No neurotics have a well balanced personality.
    Some artists are neurotic.
    Therefore: Some artists do not have a well-balanced personality.
4   All lawyers are wealthy.
    John Smith is a lawyer.
    Therefore: John Smith is wealthy.

All of these arguments are valid, but they cannot be shown to be so by the techniques of propositional logic.

We can see why this is so if we recall that in propositional logic, we do not have to notice what the propositions are about, or how they are expressed. Compound propositions are made up of simple propositions connected by the logical constants. The smallest unit is a proposition. If we were to treat these arguments as we do those we met in the preceding sections, we should have to count each proposition as simple, for they contain no logical connectives. If, since they are all different, we assign a different letter for each proposition that occurs, we shall have:

$$p$$
$$q$$
Therefore: r

This, however, is not a valid argument form, as you will see if you test it by truth-table methods. It does not have the pattern of a valid argument. Since the arguments are valid, their logical forms cannot have been correctly, that is, *completely*, displayed by treating the propositions of which they are made up as unanalysable ones. In order to show that arguments like these are valid, we need to attend to the structure of the propositions of which they are made up. We draw your attention to two features, which we shall explain in more detail in the remainder of this chapter.

First, you will see that the phrases making up the propositions show a certain recurring pattern. For example, in argument (1) the term 'voters' occurs once in each premiss but not in the conclusion. The remaining phrases making up the premisses of the argument occur once in each premiss and then recur, linked together in the conclusion. If we use abbreviatory letters for each of these terms ('R' for 'ratepayers', 'V' for 'voters' and 'C' for 'citizens') we have:

Some R are V
All V are C
Therefore: Some C are R

The form of our argument has been displayed by analysing the propositions of which the argument is composed.

Another feature to be noticed is the occurrence of the words 'all' and 'some', of which account must be taken. Statements in which these words occur are general statements. 'Some artists do not have a well balanced personality' is a general statement which we can abbreviate 'Some A are not W'. The first premiss of argument (2) No Quakers are vice traffickers is also a general statement (of the form: No Q is V).

Before we can explain how arguments of the kind we are now considering can be proved to be valid, we shall need to devote some considerable time to an examination of the structure of the propositions themselves. In the logic of propositions, all we have to attend to is the logical form of the *argument*, and this depends simply on the way in which the propositions are related by the logical constants. But at this new level of logic we need also to attend to the structure of the propositions themselves. Remember that the logic of predicates is a development of the more elementary logic of statements or propositions. We do not have to forget anything that we have learned so far. Indeed, we shall still need much of what we have already learned. But we do have to get acquainted with some new ideas.

Exercises

Extract the logical form of the following arguments using abbreviatory letters. Which of them have the same form?

1 All shareholders are entitled to vote at the AGM. All directors are shareholders. *So:* all directors are entitled to vote at the AGM.
2 No religious doctrines can be established by scientific evidence. Some religious doctrines command the assent of intelligent people. *Therefore:* some doctrines that command the assent of intelligent people cannot be established by scientific evidence.
3 No written examination is a safe test of merit. Some written

examinations demand considerable memory knowledge. *So:* some tests demanding considerable memory knowledge are not safe tests of merit.

4 All members of the Church Assembly believe in the Thirty-nine Articles. All believers in the Thirty-nine Articles appreciate theological niceties. *Therefore:* all members of the Church Assembly appreciate theological niceties.

5 All trade unions aim at the welfare of the working man. Some trade unions restrict industrial efficiency. *So:* some organisations which restrict industrial efficiency aim at the welfare of the working man.

6 If no sharks are vegetarians and all large fish in Sydney Harbour are sharks, then no large fish in Sydney Harbour are vegetarians.

7 All bishops are learned men. Some bishops believe in the existence of God. *So:* some believers in the existence of God are learned men.

8 If no capitalists are members of the Socialist Workers Party and all directors of ICI are capitalists, then no directors of ICI are members of the Socialist Workers Party.

9 No bats are feathered and all bats can fly. *Therefore:* some animals which can fly are not feathered.

10 If all astrologers are credulous and some psychiatrists are not credulous then some psychiatrists are not astrologers.

2 Predicate expressions

The first of the new ideas that we need in dealing with arguments at this new level of logic is that of a *predicate*. Any exact account of this word would involve us in difficult and controversial philosophical issues. But for the purposes of the elementary study of logic, we may understand the word in the following way.

A common sense view of the world divides it up into individual things and their properties. This rose is red; John has blue eyes and so on. An individual thing, this rose, has the property of being red; John has the property of having blue eyes, and so on.

We express these facts in sentences which say something

about the individuals, namely, that they have that particular property:

> This rose is red
> John has blue eyes
> That plant is poisonous

In old-fashioned school grammar, what is spoken about is called the subject of the sentence ('This rose', 'John', 'That plant') and what is said about the subject is called the *predicate* ('is red', 'has blue eyes', 'is poisonous'). Thus a predicate is most easily understood as a verbal expression which assigns a property to one or more individuals.

Those expressions for which we used abbreviatory letters in the preceding section are predicates. You will notice that we assign a property to a thing, not only when we say, for example, that it is red, but also when we say that it is a thing of a certain kind; as when we say of an individual that, for example, it is a swan, or that it is a man. Or, when we say of an individual that he is a Quaker, or a citizen or a ratepayer. 'Is a lawyer'; 'is a Quaker' etc. are all predicates.

It is as well to notice, although we shall not be dealing with these, that some properties are such that they can hold only of two or more individuals. For example:

> John is older than Mary
> London is larger than Exeter
> Nottingham is between Sheffield and London

To be older than or *to be larger than* are properties that hold between two individuals. In the last example, *between* is a property which holds of three things. These are known as *relational properties* because they relate two or more things. And the corresponding verbal expressions ('is larger than' and the like) are called relational predicates.

Singular propositions
When we assign a property to an individual, we may specify that individual by using a name. For example, one may say:

> Smith is bald
> Henry is a Quaker
> Red Rum is a racehorse

Or, we may specify an individual by using an individuating description, that is, a description which picks out an individual.

Examples of individuating descriptions are:

> 'The present Prime Minister of Great Britain'
> 'The tallest man in Brighton'

So, we may have:

> The tallest man in Brighton is a doctor.
> The present Prime Minister of Great Britain attended the conference.

Propositions of this kind are *singular propositions*. We can describe singular propositions in negative terms by saying:

(i) they do not contain any logical connectives
(ii) they do not contain such words as 'all', 'some', 'none' or their equivalents.

In the fourth argument on p. 137, the second premiss 'John Smith is a lawyer' and the conclusion 'John Smith is wealthy' are singular propositions.

When we break such propositions down into their parts, we do not find other propositions, but we do find what we may call *terms*. The terms are of two kinds: those which stand for individuals, which may be either names or individuating descriptions, and predicates which assign properties to those individuals.

To abbreviate the statement 'Smith is bald', we again use capitals letters for the predicates, as we did in the preceding section. For the name 'Smith', we can use the initial letter, but we shall use the lower case 's'. (We have already reserved capital letters to abbreviate predicates.) We write: Bs for

> 'Smith is bald'

To abbreviate 'The tallest man in Brighton is a doctor', we shall have to choose a letter to abbreviate the expression 'The tallest man in Brighton'. This could be 't'. 'The tallest man in Brighton is a doctor' would then be abbreviated: Dt. Please notice that it is the convention to write the predicate letter first. Do not let this confuse you.

Singular propositions may be connected by logical constants.

For example:

> Smith is a lawyer and Jones is a doctor

may be written:

> Ls . Dj

'Both Smith and Jones are bald', which is to be understood as 'Smith is bald and Jones is bald' may be written:

> Bs . Bj

We give you some exercises in abbreviating such propositions at the end of this section.

We also need to introduce symbols which will allow us to speak of any singular proposition whatsoever. (Just as, earlier, we introduced the symbols '*p*', '*q*', '*r*' to stand for any simple proposition whatsoever.) As we explained in discussing the logic of propositions, such a device will give us the means of stating general rules which apply to all statements of a given form, and will enable us to ignore the subject matter. We shall use small letters from the early part of the alphabet (*a*, *b*, *c* . . .) to stand for proper names or other expressions which stand for an individual. (In future, we shall speak simply of 'proper names' leaving 'or other expressions which pick out an individual' to be understood.) The letters '*a*', '*b*', '*c*' which stand in this way for proper names are called *individual constants*. We shall use the letters '*f*', '*g*', '*h*' to stand for predicates. We can then symbolise singular propositions by combinations like '*fa*', '*gb*', '*ha*' and so on. The symbolic expression '*fa*' will then be read as:

> *a* has the property *f*

Such symbolic expressions, which we may call *predicate formulas* will be understood as standing for *any* singular propositions, according to the meanings that we choose to assign to the letters which occur. Notice that we cannot discuss the truth or falsity of a *formula* until we *interpret* or assign a meaning to the individual constant and the predicate symbol. When we do so, we shall be speaking of the proposition which results from giving a particular interpretation to the letters of the formula.

Exercises

(A) Interpret '*f*' as 'is a lawyer'   '*a*' – 'Tom'
           '*g*' as 'is a doctor'   '*b*' – 'Dick'
           '*h*' as 'is an Indian chief'   '*c*' – 'Harry'
                                      '*d*' – 'the man with a scarred face'

Write the following in English:
     1   *fb*   2   *ga*   3   *hd*
     4   *gc*   5   *fd*   6   *hc*

(B) Using suitable letters for the individuals and predicates, express the following in logical symbolism:

1 Mary is a secretary.
2 The girl in the red dress in the corner is a journalist.
3 John is a lawyer.
4 The richest man in Bootle is a bookmaker.
5 Maledict XIV is a pope.
6 The girl in the green dress has red hair.
7 The girl in the magenta dress has red hair and bad taste.
8 The girl in the magenta dress has red hair and is either colour blind or has bad taste.
9 The best logician in Exeter plays squash.
10 Teckel is a dachshund.

3 Quantifiers

Most of the statements which make up the arguments given at the beginning of this chapter are not singular, but are *general* statements. Examples of these, taken from those arguments are:

All lawyers are wealthy.
No Quakers are drug traffickers.
Some ratepayers are voters.
Some artists do not have a well-balanced personality.

A general statement is one that does not contain any proper names, but which does contain the words 'all', 'some', 'none' or their equivalents. Our next task is to explain how statements which include such words are to be understood and symbolised. For this purpose, the statements listed above are rather too complicated, for each contains two predicate expressions. We shall begin at a simpler level, with statements which contain one predicate.

In a singular statement, as we saw in the last chapter, the individual to whom the property is assigned is named, as in: 'John is well-fed'. But in a general statement, the individual (or individuals) are not named, as in the following statements:

All individuals are well-fed.   (Everyone is well-fed)
No individual is well-fed.   (Nobody is well-fed)
Some individuals are well-fed
Some individuals are not well-fed.

We are familiar enough with such statements in ordinary discourse. We often make statements assigning properties to unnamed individuals either because we do not wish to name them or because for one reason or another we cannot do so. For example: 'Somebody robbed the bank' or 'Everyone is liable to pay income tax'.

First, we need a symbol which will stand indifferently for any individual. For this we shall use the letter 'x' (and if required, 'y' and 'z'), which is an *individual variable*. We can thus write:

All xs are well-fed
No x is well-fed

and so on. Next, we require the *quantifiers*.

(i) *The existential quantifier.* In logic we take it that by 'some'
is meant 'at least one'. When we wish to say of one or more
unspecified individuals that it or they have a certain property, we use the *existential quantifier*. This is written $(\exists x)$,
and is read: 'There is an x such that . . .' The quantifier is
prefixed to 'x is well-fed', so that we have:

$$(\exists x)(x \text{ is well-fed})$$

which is read: 'There is an x such that that x is well-fed'.
Using a capital letter to symbolise 'is well-fed', we can write:

$$(\exists x)(Wx)$$

We use the existential quantifier also to symbolise a statement like: 'Mermaids exist'. To say this is to say that there
are mermaids. It is to say, no doubt falsely, that there is at
least one individual such that that individual is a mermaid.
We symbolise this:

$$(\exists x)(Mx)$$

where 'M' abbreviates the predicate expression 'is a mermaid'.

(ii) *The universal quantifier.* When we have a statement
which includes the word 'all' or any of its equivalents, we
use the universal quantifier. 'Every individual is well-fed',
'Each individual is well-fed' say the same as 'All individuals
are well-fed'. The universal quantifier is written '(x)' and is
read:

> 'Each x is such that . . .' or
> 'For all values of x . . .' or
> 'For every x . . .'

As with the existential quantifier this is prefixed to 'x is well-
fed' to get:

$$(x) \, (x \text{ is well-fed})$$

or in English 'Everyone is well-fed'. Abbreviating 'is well-
fed' by 'W' we have:

$$(x)(Wx)$$

The universe of discourse

Now you may well feel that there is something very odd about statements like 'Everything is well-fed'. After all, it makes no sense to speak of sticks and stones as either well-fed, or not well-fed. Here we have to remember that, when we ordinarily use the words 'all' and 'every' we do so in a context. If, for instance, we read a notice 'Everything reduced in price', we take it that the individuals referred to are items which are for sale, and not, for example, shop assistants. So too in logic, except that instead of speaking of a 'context' we talk of a 'universe of discourse'.

All arguments and discussions presuppose a context. We shall assume that the *set* or *collection* of individuals which we have in mind when we use the words 'all' or 'some' is to be taken as the *universe of discourse* of the argument or discussion. So the universe of discourse consists of the kind of things we allow to be values of x. When we say: $(x)(x$ is well-fed) or $(\exists x)(x$ is well-fed) we take it that the range of things whose names can be substituted for 'x' to make singular propositions is restricted to people and/or animals. We have indicated, by using the words 'someone', 'everybody', that here the universe of discourse is people.

Even so, it may be thought, this is still not satisfactory. It is certainly false that *everyone* is well-fed, and indeed there can be very few predicates which apply to everyone. Again, we have to remember that such statements are made in a context. If a friend tells us that everyone is well, we do not dismiss his statement as almost certainly false because there are many people in the world who are not well. Rather, we understand him to mean, for example, that everyone in his family is well. The universe of discourse for 'Everyone is well-fed' may be the people in the world, the people in a given country or town, or everyone in a given family.

We shall assume throughout this book that every universe has at least one member. (Higher levels of logic do make use of so-called 'empty universes' but we shall not use them here.)

In 'Nobody is well-fed' we deny that the property of being

well-fed belongs to anybody. Here again, we use the universal quantifier:

$$(x)(x \text{ is not well fed})$$

so that we have

$$(x) \sim Wx$$

which is read: for each x, or for all values of x, x is not well-fed.

Relations between quantifiers

As with any other statement, the ones listed above can be negated. The negation of 'Everything is F' can be symbolised by placing the negation sign before the quantifier: $\sim(x)fx$. The negation of 'Everyone is well-fed', to use an example in English, is 'It is false that everyone is well-fed'. But it should be noted that 'Something is not F' also negates 'Everything is F'. ('Someone is not well-fed' negates 'Everyone is well-fed'.) This being so, the negation of 'Everything is F' can be written:

$$\text{either} \quad \sim(x)fx \quad \text{or} \quad (\exists x)\sim fx$$

The negation of 'Nothing is F' can be expressed 'It is false that nothing is F'. Or again, to use our example: the negation of 'Nobody is well-fed' can be expressed: 'It is false that nobody is well-fed'. The negation of 'Nothing is F' can be symbolised:

$$\sim(x)\sim fx$$

But 'Something is F' (Somebody is well-fed) also negates 'Nothing is F' (Nobody is well-fed):

$$(\exists x)fx$$

In fact, the quantifiers could be defined in terms of each other, as the following list of equivalences shows:

1 $(x)fx \equiv \sim(\exists x)\sim fx$
   'Everything is F' means the same as 'It is false that there is something which is not F'.

2 $(x)\sim fx \equiv \sim(\exists x)fx$
'Nothing is F' means the same as 'It is false that there is something which is F'.

3 $(\exists x)fx \equiv \sim(x)\sim fx$
'Something is F' means the same as 'It is false that everything is not F'.

4 $(\exists x)\sim fx \equiv \sim(x)fx$
'Something is not F' means the same as 'It is false that everything is F'.

Exercises

(A) Symbolise the following, using abbreviatory letters:

1 John has fair hair.
2 The largest crocodile in Africa is greedy.
3 Mary is a doctor.
4 The best soccer coach in Amherst is a philosopher.
5 Geoffrey is a logician.
6 Queen Elizabeth II is a constitutional monarch.

(B) Symbolise the following, using abbreviatory letters. Some of these propositions are negations of others in the list. Pick these out.

1 Everything changes.
2 Dragons exist.
3 Nothing changes.
4 Some things are red.
5 There are no dragons.
6 Everything is made of atoms.
7 Some things do not change.
8 There is something which is not made of atoms.

(C) Put the following propositions into logical symbolism and say which of them are equivalent:

1 Some things are red.
2 Everything is made of atoms.
3 It is false that everything is not red.
4 Some people are not well-fed.
5 It is false that something is not made of atoms.
6 It is false that everyone is well-fed.

4 Propositions with more than one predicate expression

We have now introduced all the new symbols required for symbolising the kinds of general statements which appear in our arguments. These have two predicate expressions, and to connect these, the logical constants will be required. We will take as predicate expressions '. . . is a lawyer' and '. . . is wealthy'.

'Some lawyers are wealthy' takes the existential quantifier, and is written:

$$(\exists x)(x \text{ is a lawyer and } x \text{ is wealthy})$$

Using the sign for conjunction in place of the word 'and' we have:

$$(\exists x)(x \text{ is a lawyer} . x \text{ is wealthy})$$

Please notice where we have placed the brackets. In so placing them, we show that the x of 'there is an x such that . . .' is both a lawyer and is wealthy. The *scope* of the quantifier extends to the whole of the expression within the brackets. It would not do to write:

$$(\exists x)(x \text{ is a lawyer}) . (\exists x)(x \text{ is wealthy})$$

To say that there is something which is a lawyer and that there is something which is wealthy, is *not* to say that it is one and the same thing which is both a lawyer and wealthy.

Using 'L' for 'is a lawyer' and 'W' for 'is wealthy', we can abbreviate our statement thus:

$$(\exists x)(Lx . Wx)$$

Using the letters we introduced to stand for any predicate whatsoever, we can say that any statement of the kind 'Some so-and-so is such-and-such' is to be symbolised as:

$$(\exists x)(fx . gx)$$

'Some lawyers are not wealthy' is treated in similar fashion:

(There is an x such that)(x is a lawyer but is not wealthy)

$$(\exists x)(Lx \cdot \sim Wx)$$

Any statement of the form 'Some Fs are not Gs' is symbolised

$$(\exists x)(fx \cdot \sim gx)$$

To symbolise those statements which take the universal quantifier, we use the sign for material implication. 'All lawyers are wealthy' is symbolised:

$$(x)(Lx \supset Wx)$$

We read it: (Each thing x is such that) (*if* x is a lawyer *then* x is wealthy) or

(For all values of x) (*if* x is a lawyer *then* x is wealthy)

Our universe of discourse here is *people*. But notice that, although we assume that there are people (since we assume that any universe of discourse has at least one member) we do not assume that any of these individuals are lawyers. Instead, we say that *if* any of these individuals are lawyers *then* they are wealthy. In so interpreting statements of the form: 'All *f*s are *g*s', we do not interpret them as asserting that there are any xs which have the property f, but as asserting that anything that has the property f also has the property g. If anything has the property of being a lawyer *then* he also has the property of being wealthy.

This is the way in which such statements are to be interpreted, even though in ordinary language we sometimes intend to convey more than this. Someone stating that all lawyers are wealthy might wish to imply that there are lawyers. This, however, need not cause any difficulty, for we have at our disposal a means of saying in our symbolic language that there are lawyers. This must be made explicit by adding the statement 'There are lawyers', symbolised $(\exists x)(Lx)$. In any case, many 'all' statements are made about things which do not exist. 'Everyone who has smallpox is highly contagious' is such an example. This may be true, even though there may be no one who has smallpox. Another example is: 'All dragons breathe fire'. Even though there are no dragons, it can be stated that the property of being a dragon is connected with the property of breathing fire.

So, any statement of the form 'All fs are gs' is to be rendered

$$(x)(fx \supset gx)$$

If we wish to say that there are fs, then we must write *both*:

$$1 \quad (x)(fx \supset gx)$$
$$2 \quad (\exists x)fx$$

'No lawyers are wealthy' is symbolised similarly:

$$(x)(Lx \supset \sim Wx)$$

(For all values of x, if x is a lawyer, then x is not wealthy.)

It must be stressed that it would be quite wrong to use the material implication sign, rather than the conjunction sign, for the *existential* statements. We can see this if we consider what would be meant if we rendered 'Some lawyers are wealthy' as 'There is something such that if he is a lawyer then he is wealthy', that is, $(\exists x)(Lx \supset Wx)$. It will be recalled that '$\ldots \supset \ldots$' is equivalent (by material implication) to '$\sim \ldots \lor \ldots$', and so $(\exists x)(Lx \supset Wx)$ is equivalent to $(\exists x)(\sim Lx \lor Wx)$. This says that there is something (a person) such that that person is *either* not a lawyer, *or* is wealthy. This is true of everyone who is not a lawyer, and it would be true in a world in which there were no lawyers at all. It is also true of everyone who is not a lawyer but who is wealthy. Yet clearly, 'Some lawyers are wealthy' is never intended to mean 'There is someone such that either he is not a lawyer or he is wealthy'. We mean that there is at least one person who is a lawyer and who is wealthy, and this is correctly symbolised as:

$$(\exists x)(Lx \, . \, Wx)$$

We will conclude by summarising the four kinds of statements, their symbolic expression and their equivalents:

Statement form

All *f*s are *g*s:	$(x)(fx \supset gx)$
No *f*s are *g*s:	$(x)(fx \supset \sim gx)$
Some *f*s are *g*s:	$(\exists x)(fx \cdot gx)$
Some *f*s are not *g*s:	$(\exists x)(fx \cdot \sim gx)$

Exercises

(A) Translate the following into logical symbolism:

1 All bears hibernate.
2 Men are rational.
3 Many journalists distort the truth.
4 No naturalists are unobservant.
5 Some carbon compounds are essential to life.
6 Some spaniels are not good hunters.
7 If it's gold, then it glitters.
8 All that glitters is not gold.
9 Only psychologists understand human motivation.
10 Only a minority of animals can regulate their body temperature.

(B) Express the following statements first with unnegated quantifiers and then with negated quantifiers:

1 Mermaids exist.
2 Everything changes.
3 All men are mortal.
4 No evergreens are deciduous.
5 Most journalists are unreliable.
6 There are mammals which live in water.
7 Horses are vertebrates.
8 Horses are tame.
9 Nothing is permanent.
10 If anything contains antimony, it is poisonous.

5 Translating words into symbols

We end this chapter on a cautionary note on translating ordinary English expressions into symbols. In the section on propositional logic we stressed that translating from ordinary language into symbols is not an automatic procedure.

The same is true of predicate logic. We need to take care to render the logical sense of the statement, and this requires thought.

Sentences whose correct logical translations are one of the forms so far considered, may well be expressed differently from the standard ways. This is because natural languages such as English are much richer in their acceptable modes of expression than the symbolic language of logic. For example, the sentence 'All drug pedlars are law breakers' can be expressed as:

> Drug pedlars are law breakers
> A drug pedlar is a law breaker
> All those who peddle drugs break the law
> Anyone who is a drug pedlar is a law breaker
> Drug pedlars are all law breakers

and many other ways. If you remember what we said earlier about the word 'only', you will recognize that our sentence can also be expressed:

> Only law breakers are drug pedlars.

All, however, are correctly symbolised:

$$(x)(fx \supset gx)$$

The sentence 'No Quaker is a vice trafficker' can be expressed:

> A Quaker is never a vice trafficker
> Quakers are not vice traffickers
> If a man is a Quaker, then he is no vice trafficker
> None who are Quakers are vice traffickers

And so on.
All are correctly symbolised:

$$(x)(fx \supset \sim gx)$$

Sentences of the form 'Some *f*s are *g*s' are also differently expressed. All of the following are symbolised:

$$(\exists x)(fx \cdot gx)$$

Some artists are neurotic
Many artists are neurotic
There are neurotic artists

Remember that 'Some' in logic means, by convention, 'at least one'. The branch of logic we are considering treats 'most', 'many', and 'a few' as 'some'. Some of these distinctions can be dealt with in a more advanced branch of logic called the logic of plurality.

A few variants of 'Some Fs are not Gs', symbolised $(\exists x)(fx \cdot \sim gx)$ are:

Some snakes are not poisonous
There are non-poisonous snakes
Not all snakes are poisonous
A few snakes are not poisonous

Remember that in making logical translations we have always to rely on our native speaker's understanding of the language. Here is one example of a type of statement which requires special care:

All fruits and cereals are nutritious

It is *not* correct to translate this by:

$$(x)(Fx \cdot Cx) \supset Nx$$

The latter reads: 'For all values of x, if x is a fruit *and* a cereal, then x is nutritious'. But this is not what the statement means. We are not speaking of an individual which is *both* a fruit *and* a cereal. Rather, we are saying that if anything is *either* a fruit *or* a cereal, then it is nutritious.

The *correct* way to symbolise this is:

$$(x)(Fx \vee Cx) \supset Nx$$

On the other hand, the statement:

All members who have paid their subscriptions are eligible

is correctly translated:

$$(x)(Mx \cdot Px) \supset Ex$$

For here we are speaking of an individual who is *both* a member *and* who has paid his subscription.

These last two examples introduce a type of proposition which is little more complex than those we have looked at up to now. They have *three* predicates instead of two. Further examples of statements which have more than two predicates will be found in the exercises at the end of this chapter. They require no new rules of logic to enable us to symbolise them; they call only for care in ascertaining their exact meaning.

Exercises on Part III

Translate the following into logical symbolism. Use abbreviatory letters:

1 Tray and Serafina are both dogs.
2 Ulfilas is a bishop, not a dog.
3 Alaric is a Goth and Grimalkin is a cat.
4 If Teckel is a dog, then Alaric is a Goth.
5 Ulfilas is both a bishop and a Goth.
6 Either Teckel is a dachshund or all dachshunds are brown.
7 If Teckel and Serafina are both dachshunds, then Ulfilas is a bishop.
8 If all dangerous trades should be highly paid and mining is a dangerous trade, then mining should be highly paid.
9 Some peasants are not industrious, since some of them are discontented and no one who is industrious is discontented.
10 Some reformers are fanatics, so some idealists are fanatics, since all reformers are idealists.
11 Some artists do not have a well-balanced personality, since no neurotics have a well-balanced personality and some artists are neurotic.
12 If no Quakers are vice-traffickers and all drug pedlars are vice traffickers, then no drug pedlars are Quakers.
13 All privy councillors are entitled to be called 'right honourable' but some privy councillors are not honourable men.
14 All liquids are incompressible and exhibit surface tension.
15 All solids are either crystalline or amorphous.
16 Most nitrates and phosphates are useful fertilisers.
17 All crocodiles and alligators are carnivores.

18 Everything that is much advertised is expensive. Some expensive things are rare. All rare and expensive things are sought after. So, some things that are much advertised are sought after.

19 All journalists are sensation-mongers. All who are journalists and sensation-mongers are unscrupulous. So, if anyone is a journalist, he is both unscrupulous and a sensation-monger.

20 All nitrates and phosphates are good fertilisers. All good fertilisers are needed by farmers. Some phosphates are cheap. *Therefore:* Some things that are cheap are needed by farmers.

Part IV

The Logic of Predicates (2)

1- Now that we have seen how simple statements which include quantifiers are to be analysed, we can turn to the arguments which have these statements as premisses and conclusion. First we should note an important difference between the logic of propositions and the logic of predicates. In propositional logic, we began by constructing truth-tables to determine whether or not a given argument was a valid one. There is no such convenient procedure in predicate logic and, indeed, there is no general decision procedure for this branch of logic. We can therefore begin straight away by explaining how we can construct proofs that a given conclusion follows from a given set of premisses.

The method of constructing proofs in predicate logic is much the same as in the logic of propositions. That is to say, it is not an automatic procedure like the construction of truth tables but requires thought and the application of rules. The nineteen rules that we used in propositional logic are used also in the logic of predicates. But we need additional rules to deal with the quantifiers. Perhaps you can see, in the following argument, that the conclusions would appear to follow from the premisses by the rule of hypothetical syllogism, were it not for the quantifiers:

All directors are shareholders.

All shareholders are entitled to vote at the AGM

Therefore: All directors are entitled to vote at the AGM

In symbols, we have:

$$1 \quad (x)(Dx \supset Sx)$$
$$2 \quad (x)(Sx \supset Vx)$$
$$\therefore (x)(Dx \supset Vx)$$

Our additional rules will permit us to drop and replace quantifiers.

Besides giving the rules, we shall explain and justify their use. We shall begin with the rule which permits us to drop the universal quantifier, *Universal Instantiation*. Now you may wish to ask why, if we are allowed to drop and replace quantifiers, it was necessary to introduce them in the first place. In explaining the rule of *Universal Instantiation* (UI, for short), we shall try to answer this question.

2 Universal instantiation

Let us start by taking the statement 'Everyone is hungry', symbolised:

$$(x)Hx$$

and let us suppose that we have a restricted universe of discourse limited to a group of friends: Tom, Dick and Harry. 'Everyone is hungry' will be true if and only if each individual in the universe is hungry. Since there are but three individuals in our universe, 'Everyone is hungry' will be true if and only if Tom is hungry and Dick is hungry and Harry is hungry. We can symbolise this as follows:

$$(x)Hx$$

which will be true if and only if

$$Ht . Hd . Hh$$

The universal proposition is equivalent to the conjunction

of singular propositions in which the predicate 'H' is assigned to each individual in the universe. If we know that all members of a given universe have a certain property, we know also that *any* member of that universe will have that property. The same is true of universal propositions in which there are two or more predicate expressions. Take, for example, 'Everyone who went to the match is hungry' symbolised:

$$(x)(Mx \supset Hx)$$

This is equivalent to:

$$(Mt \supset Ht) \cdot (Md \supset Hd) \cdot (Mh \supset Hh)$$

where, as we are supposing, Tom, Dick and Harry are all the members of the universe.

The rule of Universal Instantiation permits us to replace the quantified expression

$$(x)Hx$$

with a singular statement assigning the predicate 'H' to a named member of the universe. In our example, we may infer, from '$(x)Hx$', 'Ht' or, of course, 'Hd' or 'Hh'.

Let us see how this works with a simple argument:

  1 Everyone who went to the match is hungry.
  2 Tom went to the match.
Therefore: Tom is hungry.

In symbols:

    1 $(x)(Mx \supset Hx)$
    2 Mt

                    $\therefore Ht$

The conclusion can be shown to follow from the premisses in the following way:

    1 $(x)(Mx \supset Hx)$
    2 Mt
    3 $Mt \supset Ht$ (from 1, by Universal Instantiation.)
    4 Ht (from 2 and 3 by *Modus ponens*.)

Now it is quite true that we could have proved that this particular argument was valid within propositional logic. Since we have restricted the universe of discourse to three members, the universal proposition

$$(x)(Mx \supset Hx)$$

is equivalent to the conjunction of three propositions:

$$(Mt \cdot Ht) \cdot (Md \supset Hd) \cdot (Mh \supset Hh)$$

And you may think that we could have taken this conjunction as the first premiss of the argument and not bothered to introduce the quantifier at all. But there are good reasons for not proceeding in this way.

In the first place, in most of the arguments that we meet and in most of the 'All' statements that we make, the universe of discourse is not limited, as in our example, to three or even to four or five members. Take for example, 'all men are mortal'. Using 'D' for 'mortal' (to avoid confusion with 'M' for 'men'), this is symbolised:

$$(x)(Mx \supset Dx)$$

and is read:

For every individual x, if that x is a man, then that x is mortal.

The individuals in this case are living creatures. Our statement is equivalent to the conjunction of a set of statements like: If individual a_1 is a man, then a_1 is mortal – thus:

$$(Ma_1 \supset Da_1) \cdot (Ma_2 \supset Da_2) \cdot (Ma_2 \supset Da_2) \cdot (Ma_n \supset Da_n)$$

where a_1, a_2 and so on are individual constants, symbols which stand for names of the individuals in the universe and 'a_n' is the name of the last individual, however many there may be. Quite clearly, it is impossible in practice to set out all of the statements which will be true of individual living things if our quantified statement is true. And since we cannot set out the conjunction in the case of a large universe of discourse, as we could with the one restricted to Tom, Dick and Harry, we cannot do without the quantifiers.

So far we have talked rather informally about the quantifiers. We have now to give some rules for their use which will enable us to deal with a wide range of arguments in predicate logic. If we were to give a completely adequate account of the rules for dropping and replacing quantifiers, we should meet some rather complex issues in predicate logic. And it would be quite out of place in an elementary and practical treatment of symbolic logic to raise these issues. So we shall have to forego a completely adequate account, that is, an account which will provide for all the possible arguments that can be met in the logic of predicates. Instead, we shall be content with a treatment that will meet the needs of all the arguments that will occur in this book.

To state the rule of Universal Instantiation we have to introduce a new symbol. We want to be able to move, in accordance with a rule from expressions like:

$$(x)Mx, (x)(Mx \supset Dx), (x)(Mx \lor Hx) \text{ and the like}$$

to their corresponding instantiations:

$$Ma, Ma \supset Da, Mb \lor Hb \text{ and so on.}$$

We shall introduce the Greek letter ϕ to stand for the predicate or predicates in such expressions, so that the general form of a universally quantified expression becomes:

$$(x)\phi x$$

We now have to explain in more detail than we have done so far how we get rid of the universal quantifier. In the arguments that we looked at above, we moved from an expression of the form:

$$(x)\phi x$$

to an expression of the form:

$$\phi a$$

where the '*a*' is an individual constant which stands for a particular individual. In fact, in the examples above, we used the initial letters of the names Tom, Dick and Harry for our individual constants. So we went from:

$$(x)(Mx \supset Hx)$$

to: $$Mt \supset Ht$$

But we also need another kind of symbol for individuals. If we know that all the members of our universe have a certain property, we can certainly conclude, as we did, that a particular member, say, Tom, has that property. But we can also conclude that *any* member, taken at random, has the property. We can say, in other words: 'Take any individual you like in that universe.' For example, in the universe of albino rats, it is true that every individual has forty-two chromosomes. We can make statements about individuals in that universe in two ways. We may say, first, 'Take Whiskers', a particular rat: it is true that

Whiskers has forty-two chromosomes

But, we can also say: 'Take any rat you like':

Any rat you like has forty-two chromosomes

Both statements are true and both clearly follow from the general statement:

For all *x*, if *x* is a rat, then *x* has forty-two chromosomes

We need to be able to distinguish our referring to particular named members of the universe from referring to any individual taken at random. For the latter case we shall use the lower case letter '*z*'. Now we can distinguish between:

A given individual has the property

and:

Any individual you like has the property

by representing the first as:

$$\phi a$$

and the second as:

$$\phi z$$

We can now state our rule as follows:

Universal Instantiation (UI)
From '$(x)\phi x$' we may infer either 'ϕa' or 'ϕz'.

The importance of the introduction of 'z' as a second type of individual symbol will become clear in the next section when we introduce the rule of *Universal Generalisation* (UG, for short.)

Universal generalisation

The rule of *Universal Generalisation* permits us to move from a statement about an individual, whether named or taken at random, to a statement about all individuals in the universe. It permits us to move from an unquantified statement to a universally quantified one. And here we can see the importance of distinguishing between a statement about a *named* individual and one which ascribes a predicate to 'any individual you care to take'.

First consider the statement: Whiskers has forty-two chromosomes, which we symbolise:

$$Cw$$

Or we could take the statement 'Tom is hungry' symbolised as

$$Ht$$

Clearly, if we know only that Whiskers, who is a rat, has forty-two chromosomes we cannot conclude from that alone that all his fellow rats do so as well. From 'Tom is hungry' we cannot conclude that everybody is hungry, even if 'everybody' includes just Tom, Dick and Harry. The rule of Universal Generalisation does *not* permit us to infer 'Everybody is . . .' or 'All are . . .' from the fact that some named person or individual has the property in question. From 'ϕa' we may *not* infer '$(x)\phi x$'.

However, if any rat, taken at random, has a certain property then all individuals in the universe of rats have that property. Accordingly, the rule of *Universal Generalisation* can be expressed:

From 'ϕz' we may infer '$(x)\phi x$'

Here is an example where both rules are required:

All directors are shareholders
All shareholders are entitled to vote at the AGM
Therefore: all directors are entitled to vote at the AGM.

In symbols:

$$1 \quad (x)(Dx \supset Sx)$$
$$2 \quad (x)(Sx \supset Vx)$$
$$\therefore (x)(Dx \supset Vx)$$

The proof is as follows:

$$3 \quad Dz \supset Sz \qquad 1,UI$$
$$4 \quad Sz \supset Vz \qquad 2,UI$$
$$5 \quad Dz \supset Vz \qquad 3,4,HS$$
$$6 \quad (x)(Dx \supset Vx) \qquad 5,UG$$

You will notice that at line 3 we have substituted '$Dz \supset Sz$' for the first premiss. We have chosen the symbol for 'any individual taken at random' rather than an individual constant, although the UI rule permits us to use either. We have done this because the conclusion required is a universally quantified expression. Had we chosen '$Da \supset Sa$' to instantiate the first premiss and '$Sa \supset Va$' to instantiate the second, we could have reached line 5 of the proof by Hypothetical Syllogism but we could not have generalised that line. For the UG rule does not permit us to infer '$(x)(Dx \supset Vx)$' from '$Da \supset Va$' or from any other formula containing an individual constant (for example, '$\sim Da \lor Va$').

If the conclusion is a singular proposition, as in the previous example on p. 16I, we infer 'ϕa' from '$(x)\phi x$'.

Before we give you some examples to work for yourself, here is another:

All historians are scholars; so, no one who is not a scholar is an historian.

First the argument is symbolised:

$$1 \quad (x)(Hx \supset Sx)$$
$$\therefore (x)(\sim Sx \supset \sim Hx)$$

The proof proceeds as follows. Noting that we are to derive a universally quantified conclusion, we instantiate the premiss thus:

$$2 \quad Hz \supset Sz \qquad 1,UI$$
$$3 \quad \sim Sz \supset \sim Hz \quad 2,Trans.$$

From line 3 the conclusion can be derived by UG, so that our proof is:

$$1 \quad (x)(Hx \supset Sx) \qquad \therefore (x)(\sim Sx \supset \sim Hx)$$
$$2 \quad Hz \supset Sz \qquad 1,UI$$
$$3 \quad \sim Sz \supset \sim Hz \qquad 2,Trans.$$
$$4 \quad (x)(\sim Sx \supset \sim Hx) \quad 3,UG$$

Exercises

Translate the following arguments into logical form and prove the conclusions:

1 No politicians are honourable and all Members of Parliament are politicians. *So:* no Members of Parliament are honourable.
2 All believers in human equality are defenders of democracy. All Quakers are believers in human equality. *So:* All Quakers are defenders of democracy.
3 No Indo-European languages are tone languages. All Chinese dialects are tone languages. *So:* no Chinese dialects are Indo-European.
4 All historians are scholars and no scholar fails to check his

sources. *So:* no one who fails to check his sources is an historian.

5   No defenders of democracy are fascists or communists. All believers in human equality are defenders of democracy. *So:* no believers in human equality are fascists.

6   All Aztecs and Toltecs were pre-Columbian inhabitants of Mexico. All pre-Columbian inhabitants of Mexico cultivated maize and practised human sacrifice. *So:* all Toltecs practised human sacrifice.

7   All scientists respect truth and seek it. No journalists respect truth. *So:* No scientists are journalists.

8   All members of the Athenaeum are wealthy and well-educated. *So:* if anyone is not wealthy, he is not a member of the Athenaeum.

9   No psychopath has any regard for others. All without regard for others are anti-social and dangerous. All dangerous people require supervision. *So:* All psychopaths require supervision.

3   Existential propositions

We shall take as our example 'Someone is hungry', where our universe of discourse, as before, is the group of people, Tom, Dick and Harry. If 'Someone is hungry is true, then at least one of the following singular propositions is true:

'Tom is hungry'; 'Dick is hungry'; 'Harry is hungry'.

In symbols:

$$(\exists x)Hx$$

can be reduced to:

$$Ht \lor Hd \lor Hh$$

Similarly 'Someone went to the match and is hungry' can be reduced to:

'Tom went to the match and is hungry *or* Dick went to the match and is hungry *or* Harry went to the match and is hungry.'

In symbols:

$$(\exists x)(Mx \, . \, Hx)$$

can be reduced to disjunctions of singular propositions:

$$(Mt \cdot Ht) \lor (Md \cdot Hd) \lor (Mh \cdot Hh)$$

Now let us change our example to one where the universe of discourse is not limited as is the one above. Let us take

'Some roses are yellow'

where the universe of discourse is flowers. In symbols, we have:

$$(\exists x)(Rx \cdot Yx)$$

As before this is reducible to disjunctions of singular propositions:

$$(Ra_1 \cdot Ya_1) \lor (Ra_2 \cdot Ya_2) \lor \ldots (Ra_n \cdot Ya_n)$$

That is; flower a_1 is a rose and is yellow *or* flower a_2 is a rose and is yellow *or* . . . and so on.

Existential instantiation

If it is true that some roses are yellow, then it will be true that at least one flower that is a rose is yellow, whether that flower is flower a_1 or flower a_2 or . . . flower a_n. The rule of Existential Instantiation permits us to substitute for '$(\exists x)(Rx \cdot Yx)$' a singular statement naming some particular flower or other. That is, from '$(\exists x)(Rx \cdot Yx)$' we may infer '$Ra_1 \cdot Ya_1$ *or* $Ra_2 \cdot Ya_2$ or . . .' Generally, we may say that from:

$$(\exists x)\phi x$$

we may infer:

$$\phi a$$

where 'a' is an individual constant, that is, a substitute for a name. However, there is an important restriction to be placed on this rule, namely, that the individual constant 'a' must not have occurred previously in the proof. (We shall explain later why this restriction is necessary.) Accordingly, we can express the rule of Existential Instantiation as follows:

From '$(\exists x)\phi x$' we may infer 'ϕa' provided that 'a' does not occur previously in the proof.

Notice that we are *not* licensed to infer 'ϕz' from '$(\exists x)\phi x$'. We have agreed that 'z' is not a symbol for the name of an individual but a symbol for *any* individual taken at random. Clearly, from the information that some roses are yellow we are not entitled to infer that any rose, taken at random, is yellow.

Existential generalisation

Existential generalisation is quite straightforward. If we are given the information, that, for example, Tom went to the match, we are entitled to infer that someone went to the match. If we are given the information that flower a_1 is a rose and is yellow, we are entitled to infer that some roses are yellow. (Remember that in logic 'some' means 'at least one'.) The rule for Existential Generalisation may be expressed:

From ϕa or from ϕz we may infer '$(\exists x)\phi x$'.

Here is an example in which three of the four rules are used, UI, EI and EG.

Some proteins are poisonous.
All proteins contain nitrogen.
Therefore: some substances containing nitrogen are poisonous.

In logical notation we have:

1   $(\exists x)(Px \, . \, Vx)$
2   $(x)(Px \supset Nx)$

            $(\exists x)(Nx \, . \, Vx)$

The proof continues:

3   $Pa \, . \, Va$ 1,EI
4   $Pa \supset Na$ 2,UI

5	Pa	3,Simp.
6	Na	4,5,MP
7	Va . Pa	3,Comm.
8	Va	7,Simp.
9	Na . Va	6,8,Conj.
10	(∃x)(Nx . Vx)	9,EG

Here are some exercises. Notice that in all of them the existential proposition must be instantiated first. This is connected with the restriction on EI which we shall explain in the next chapter.

Exercises

Translate the following arguments into logical form and prove the conclusions:

1 No naturalists are unobservant. Some unobservant people are interested in animals. *So:* some people who are interested in animals are not naturalists.

2 All ratepayers are entitled to vote in municipal elections. Some parliamentary electors are not entitled to vote in municipal elections. *So:* some parliamentary electors are not ratepayers.

3 All bishops are learned men. Some Christians are bishops. *Therefore:* some Christians are learned men.

4 No religious doctrines can be established by scientific evidence. Some religious doctrines command the assent of intelligent people. *So:* some doctrines that command the assent of intelligent people cannot be established by scientific evidence.

5 No neurotics have a well-balanced personality. Some artists are neurotic. *So:* Some artists do not have a well-balanced personality.

6 All trade unions aim at the welfare of the working man. Some trade unions restrict industrial efficiency. *So:* some organisations which restrict industrial efficiency aim at the welfare of the working man.

7 All theories based on empirical evidence deserve rational consideration. Some psychological theories do not deserve

rational consideration. *So:* some psychological theories are
not based on empirical evidence.

8 Some criminals are psychopathic and dangerous. All who
are psychopathic are incurable. *Therefore:* some criminals
are incurable.

9 Everyone who went to the match has not eaten for six hours.
If anyone is not hungry, then he has eaten in the last six
hours. Tom went to the match. *So:* Tom is hungry.

10 Socrates was a Greek. All Greeks lived in slave societies.
None who lived in slave societies believed in human rights.
So: Socrates did not believe in human rights.

4 Using the rule of existential instantiation

We must now explain the restriction imposed on the EI
rule: From '$(\exists x)\phi x$' we may infer 'ϕa', *provided that there
is no previous occurrence of 'a' in the proof.*

If there were no such restriction, we should be able to
'prove' conclusions from premises in patently invalid arguments.

Consider the following argument, which is clearly invalid:

> Some thrushes eat snails.
> Some Frenchmen eat snails.
> *Therefore:* Some thrushes are Frenchmen.

We may formalise this as:

1 $(\exists x)(Tx . Sx)$
2 $(\exists x)(Fx . Sx)$

$(\exists x)(Tx . Fx)$

If we ignore the restriction on EI, we can 'prove' the conclusion from the given premises as follows:

3 $Ta . Sa$ 1,EI
4 $Fa . Sa$ 2,EI (ignoring the restriction)
5 Ta 3,Simp.
6 Fa 4,Simp.
7 $Ta . Fa$ 5,6,Conj.
8 $(\exists x)(Tx . Fx)$ 7,EG

Clearly, we cannot have a rule that will not allow us to distinguish between valid and invalid arguments and here we have 'proved' a patently false conclusion from two true premisses. So, Existential Instantiation has a restriction.

Consider what we did in the example above. At line 3, we used EI to instantiate line 1. From '$(\exists x)(Tx \cdot Sx)$' we inferred '$Ta \cdot Sa$'. We used the individual constant 'a', which is a substitute for a name, to select a particular individual. Line 3 reads, in English, 'a is a thrush and a eats snails'. But having used the name 'a' once we cannot go on, without fatal ambiguity, to use the *same* name again with a different application. Yet this is just what we have done in line 4 where we have used the same name 'a' for a Frenchman. Thus line 4 is an illegitimate step. We could, by observing the restriction on EI, have introduced a *second* individual constant by a second use of EI so that:

$$4 \quad Fb \cdot Sb \quad 2,\text{EI}$$

would be permissible. But then we should not then be able to derive the desired conclusion. And this, of course, is as it should be, for the conclusion does not follow from the premisses – the argument is invalid.

Because of this restriction, we need to exercise care over the individual constants introduced by UI. For example, suppose we want to show the following argument to be valid by deriving the conclusion from the premisses:

> All nuclear devices are dangerous
> Some power sources are nuclear devices
> *Therefore:* some power sources are dangerous

In symbols, this becomes:

$$1 \quad (x)(Nx \supset Dx)$$
$$2 \quad (\exists x)(Px \cdot Nx)$$
$$(\exists x)(Px \cdot Dx)$$

If, as is not unnatural, we begin with line 1 and instantiate according to the UI rule, we get:

$$3 \quad Na \supset Da$$

But, remembering the restriction on EI, we cannot write line 4 as:

$$4 \quad Pa . Na$$

for we have already used 'a' in the proof. (Nor would it help to use 'z' for 'a' at step 3, for then we could not get to our conclusion.) *Always remember that proof in logic is a matter of strict application of rules.*

In this example, to avoid infringing our rules, we must use EI *first*:

1	$(x)(Nx \supset Dx)$	
2	$(\exists x)(Px . Nx)$	
		$\therefore (\exists x)(Px . Dx)$
3	$Pa . Na$	2,EI
4	$Na \supset Da$	1,UI
5	$Na . Pa$	3,Comm.
6	Na	5,Simp.
7	Da	4,6,MP
8	$Pa . Da$	8,7,Conj.
9	$(\exists x)(Px . Dx)$	9,EG

Remember: use EI before UI and do not use EI more than once in any proof.

Here are the four rules for dealing with quantifiers:

Universal Instantiation (UI)
From '$(x)\phi x$' we may infer 'ϕa' or 'ϕz'

Universal Generalisation (UG)
From 'ϕz' we may infer '$(x)\phi x$'.

Existential Instantiation (EI)
From '$(\exists x)\phi x$' we may infer 'ϕa' provided that 'a' does not occur previously in the proof.

Existential Generalisation (EG)
From 'ϕa' or from 'ϕz' we may infer '$(\exists x)\phi x$.

With these four rules governing quantifiers in addition to the nineteen rules that we used for propositional logic, we can deal with a wide variety of arguments. For example:

1   Anyone who is intelligent and hard-working will be successful if he is lucky. *Therefore:* if anyone is lucky but not successful, either he is not intelligent or not hard-working.

  1   $(x)[(\mathrm{I}x \,.\, \mathrm{H}x) \supset (\mathrm{L}x \supset \mathrm{S}x)]$

                   $\therefore$ $(x)[(\mathrm{L}x \,.\, {\sim}\mathrm{S}x) \supset ({\sim}\mathrm{I}x \lor {\sim}\mathrm{H}x)]$

  2   $(\mathrm{I}z \,.\, \mathrm{H}z) \supset (\mathrm{L}z \supset \mathrm{S}z)$ 1,UI

  3   ${\sim}(\mathrm{L}z \supset \mathrm{S}z) \supset {\sim}(\mathrm{I}z \,.\, \mathrm{H}z)$ 2,Trans.

  4   ${\sim}(\mathrm{L}z \supset \mathrm{S}z) \supset ({\sim}\mathrm{I}z \lor {\sim}\mathrm{H}z)$ 3,de M.

  5   ${\sim}({\sim}\mathrm{L}z \lor \mathrm{S}z) \supset ({\sim}\mathrm{I}z \lor {\sim}\mathrm{H}z)$ 4,Impl.

  6   $(\mathrm{L}z \,.\, {\sim}\mathrm{S}z) \supset ({\sim}\mathrm{I}z \lor {\sim}\mathrm{H}z)$ 5,de M,DN

  7   $(x)[(\mathrm{L}x \,.\, {\sim}\mathrm{S}x) \supset ({\sim}\mathrm{I}x \lor {\sim}\mathrm{H}x)]$ 6,UG

2   All nitrates and phosphates are good fertilisers. All good fertilisers are needed by farmers. Some phosphates are cheap. *Therefore:* Some things that are cheap are needed by farmers.

This becomes:

  1   $(x)(\mathrm{N}x \lor \mathrm{P}x) \supset \mathrm{G}x$

  2   $(x)(\mathrm{G}x \supset \mathrm{F}x)$

  3   $(\exists x)(\mathrm{P}x \,.\, \mathrm{G}x)$

                   $\therefore$ $(\exists x)(\mathrm{G}x \,.\, \mathrm{F}x)$

  4   $\mathrm{P}a \,.\, \mathrm{G}a$ 3,EI (Note that we use EI first)

  5   $(\mathrm{N}a \lor \mathrm{P}a) \supset \mathrm{G}a$ 1,UI

  6   $(\mathrm{G}a \supset \mathrm{F}a)$ 2,UI

  7   $\mathrm{G}a$ 4,Comm., Simp.

  8   $\mathrm{F}a$ 6,9,MP

  9   $\mathrm{G}a \,.\, \mathrm{F}a$ 10,11,Conj.

10   $(\exists x)(\mathrm{G}x \,.\, \mathrm{F}x)$ 12,EG

3   All cats and dogs are carnivores. Some dogs are dachshunds. Some dogs are hunters. All carnivores are hunters.

So: Some dachshunds are hunters.

This becomes:

1 $(x)(Dx \lor Fx) \supset Cx$
2 $(\exists x)(Dx \cdot Tx)$
3 $(\exists x)(Dx \cdot Hx)$
4 $(x)(Cx \supset Hx)$

$\therefore (\exists x)(Tx \cdot Hx)$

Notice that 2 and 3 both have the existential quantifier. So we can use EI on only one of them. Which one we choose will depend on which of them is the more useful for our proof.

5 $Da \cdot Ta$ 2,EI

(We choose to apply EI to 2 because though we need both Ta and Ha for our conclusion, we can obtain Ha otherwise than by using EI.)

6 $(Da \lor Fa) \supset Ca$ 1,UI
7 $Ca \supset Ha$ 4,UI
8 Da 5,Simp.
9 $Da \lor Fa$ 8,Add.
10 Ca 6,9,MP
11 Ha 7,10,MP (We have thus obtained Ha without the use of EI on 3)
12 Ta 5,Comm.,Simp.
13 $Ta \cdot Ha$ 11,12,Conj.
14 $(\exists x)(Tx \cdot Hx)$ 13,EG

Exercises

Prove the validity of the following arguments by the rules of the logic of predicates, that is, the quantifier rules and the nineteen rules of propositional logic.

1 No proteins contain phosphorus. Some substances containing phosphorus are poisonous. *So:* Some poisonous substances are not proteins.
2 All leopards and cheetahs are carnivores. Some leopards are spotted. Some leopards eat zebras. All carnivores eat zebras. *So:* some spotted creatures eat zebras.

3 All journalists distort the truth. Some historians do not distort the truth. *So:* some historians are not journalists.

4 No sharks are vegetarians. All large fish in Sydney Harbour are sharks. *Therefore:* no large fish in Sydney Harbour are vegetarians.

5 All diplomats are courteous. Some diplomats are extroverts. All courteous extroverts are popular. *So:* some diplomats are popular.

Establish the validity of the following argument forms:

6 $(x)(Px \supset Lx)$
   $(x)[(Lx . Px) \supset Sx]$
   $\therefore (x)[(Px \supset (Lx . Sx)]$

7 $(x)[(Hx . Bx) \supset (Wx . Cx)]$
   $(x)[(Hx . Ex) \supset Bx]$
   $\therefore (x)[(Hx . Ex) \supset Wx]$

8 $(x)[(Tx \supset (Fx . Dx)]$
   $(\exists x)(Ex . Tx)$
   $\therefore (\exists x)(Ex . Dx)$

9 $(x)[(Bx \lor Gx) \supset Fx]$
   $(x)[(Fx \lor Vx) \supset Nx]$
   $\therefore (x)(Bx \supset Nx)$

10 $(x)[(Cx \supset (Fx \lor Kx)]$
    $(x)(Fx \supset Nx)$
    $(\exists x)(Cx . {\sim}Nx)$
    $(\exists x)(Cx . Kx)$

5 Arguments with universal premises and particular conclusions

Throughout our discussion of quantified propositions, we have been stressing that statements of the type 'All *f*s are *g*s' do not assert the existence of *f*s. 'All cyanides are poisonous' for example, is to be understood as:

For any *x*, if that *x* is a cyanide, then that *x* is poisonous

It is not stated that there are any cyanides or, indeed, any poisonous things. We cannot infer from 'All cyanides are poisonous' by itself that some cyanides are poisonous. From one or more universal propositions, we cannot infer the existence of anything.

Yet the following argument *seems* to be valid:

All trade unions aim at the welfare of the workers.
All trade unions restrict industrial efficiency.
Therefore: some things that restrict industrial efficiency
aim at the welfare of the workers.

We can symbolise this as follows:

$$1 \quad (x)(Tx \supset Wx)$$
$$2 \quad (x)(Tx \supset Rx)$$
$$\therefore (\exists x)(Rx \cdot Wx)$$

Although the argument seems to be valid, it is not; for we
cannot derive an existential conclusion from universal premisses.

The difficulty is caused by the fact that most common
sense reasoning assumes that what we are talking about –
trade unions in this case – really exist. But neither of our
premisses asserts that there are trades unions. The first says
simply that for any x (assuming our universe to be organisations), that if x is a trades union, then it aims at the welfare
of the workers. This is not a defect of modern logic. Indeed,
it is useful to be able to formulate our arguments in a way
that does not oblige us to assume or to enquire into the
existence of what we are arguing about. For example: the
argument:

If all vampires have blood group KZ and all who have
group KZ are immortal, then all vampires are immortal

is a valid one even though vampires, blood group KZ and
immortal creatures do not exist. (Remember that in logic
we are concerned with validity and not with factual truth.)

In the argument about trades unions above, we can per-
fectly well accommodate common sense by adding, as an
extra premiss:

Trade unions exist

thus making our assumption explicit. We can always prove
the conclusions of such arguments if we add an extra pre-

miss to the effect that there exist instances of one of the terms in question. Here is the proof of the argument about trades unions:

1	$(x)(Tx \supset Wx)$	
2	$(x)(Tx \supset Rx)$	
		$\therefore (\exists x)(Rx . Wx)$
3	$(\exists x)Tx$	*Existential assumption*
4	Ta	3,EI (NB: used first!)
5	$Ta \supset Wa$	1,UI
6	$Ta \supset Ra$	2,UI
7	Wa	4,5,MP
8	Ra	4,6,MP
9	$Ra . Wa$	7,8,Conj.
10	$(\exists x)(Rx . Wx)$	9,EG

Exercises

Express the following arguments in logical symbolism and prove that they are valid:

1 If no defenders of democracy are fascists and all defenders of democracy are believers in human equality, some believers in human equality are not fascists.
2 All proteins contain nitrogen. All proteins are combinations of amino-acids. *Therefore:* some substances containing nitrogen are combinations of amino-acids.
3 No proteins contain heavy metals. Everything containing heavy metals is poisonous. *So:* some poisons are not proteins.
4 All fruits and vegetables are nutritious. All nutritious substances contain proteins. Everything containing proteins is liable to decay. *So:* some vegetables are liable to decay.
5 All frogs, toads and salamanders are amphibians. All amphibians have a three-chambered heart. *So:* some creatures having a three-chambered heart are salamanders.

Proof in predicate logic

We now have at our disposal rules which are adequate to deal with many of the simpler proof patterns of predicate logic. We need the rules that we used in the logic of propositions together with the simplified quantifier rules that we have discussed above. In addition, we can use the useful technique of conditional proof that we met in the logic of propositions. We can use this method even when the conclusion we are trying to prove is *not* in conditional form. Suppose we wish to reach a step in the argument which is in conditional form. We can introduce the antecedent of this conditional in the usual way and so prove our conditional. We can then go on to use this conditional to prove the desired conclusion. Example 3 on p. 183 uses this device. (For the proof, see pp. 261–2.)

1 Some vampires are respectable persons in Hampstead. All respectable persons in Hampstead are either doctors or solicitors. No vampire is a solicitor. If anyone is a doctor, then if he performs an illegal transfusion, he is struck off by the GMC. All vampires perform illegal transfusions. *Therefore:* Some vampires are struck off by the GMC.

This becomes:

1	$(\exists x)(Vx \cdot Rx)$	
2	$(x)[(Rx \supset (Dx \lor Sx)]$	
3	$(x)(Vx \supset \sim Sx)$	
4	$(x)[Dx \supset (Ix \supset Gx)]$	
5	$(x)(Vx \supset Ix)$	$/\therefore (\exists x)(Vx \cdot Gx)$
6	$Va \cdot Ra$	1,EI
7	$Ra \supset (Da \lor Sa)$	2,UI
8	$Va \supset \sim Sa$	3,UI
9	Va	6,Simp.
10	$\sim Sa$	8,9,MP
11	Ra	6,Comm.,Simp.
12	$Da \lor Sa$	7,11,MP
13	Da	12,10,Comm.,DS
14	$Da \supset (Ia \supset Ga)$	4,UI
15	$Ia \supset Ga$	13,14,MP
16	$Va \supset Ia$	5,UI

17	I*a*	9,16,MP
18	G*a*	15,17,MP
19	V*a* . G*a*	9,18,Conj.
20	(∃*x*)(V*x* . G*x*)	19,EG

2 Some vampires live in Transylvania. All who live in Transylvania have either a Rumanian passport or a Hungarian passport. No vampires have a Hungarian passport. No one who can fly needs to respect international borders. All vampires can fly. No one needs a passport unless he has to respect international borders. *Therefore:* some vampires have a Rumanian passport but do not need one.

1	(∃*x*)(V*x* . T*x*)	
2	(*x*)[T*x* ⊃ (R*x* ∨ H*x*)]	
3	(*x*)(V*x* ⊃ ~H*x*)	
4	(*x*)(F*x* ⊃ ~B*x*)	
5	(*x*)(V*x* ⊃ F*x*)	
6	(*x*)(N*x* ⊃ B*x*)	/∴ (∃*x*)(V*x* . R*x* . ~N*x*)
7	V*a* . T*a*	1,EI
8	T*a*	7,Comm.,Simp.
9	T*a* ⊃ (R*a* v H*a*)	2,UI
10	R*a* v H*a*	7,8,MP
11	V*a* ⊃ ~H*a*	3,UI
12	V*a*	7,Simp.
13	~H*a*	11,12,MP
14	R*a*	9,13,Comm.,DS
15	V*a* ⊃ F*a*	5,UI
16	F*a*	12,15,MP
17	F*a* ⊃ ~B*a*	4,UI
18	~B*a*	16,17,MP
19	N*a* ⊃ B*a*	6,UI
20	~N*a*	18,19,MT
21	V*a* . R*a* . ~N*a*	12,14,20,Conj.
22	(∃*x*)(V*x* . R*x* . ~N*x*)	20,EG

3 All vampires and werewolves are bad neighbours and unsocial. *Therefore*: All werewolves are bad neighbours.

$$1 \quad (x)[(Vx \lor Wx) \supset (Bx \cdot Ux)]$$
$$\therefore (x)(Wx \supset Bx)$$

→2	Wz	
3	$(Vz \lor Wz) \supset (Bz \cdot Uz)$	1,UI
4	$Vz \lor Wz$	2,Add.,Comm.
5	$Bz \cdot Uz$	3,4,MP
6	Bz	5,Simp.
7	$Wz \supset Bz$	2–6,CP
8	$(x)(Wx \supset Bx)$	7,UG

Here we have indicated the introduction of the assumption for our conditional proof by a horizontal arrow at 2 and joined it by a vertical line to the horizontal line at 6 which shows the end of the scope of the assumption.

4 No bishops live on human blood. *Therefore:* If Dracula is a vampire, then if all vampires live on human blood, Dracula is not a bishop.

$$1 \quad (x)(Bx \supset \sim Hx)$$
$$\therefore (Vd \supset ((x)(Vx \supset Hx) \supset \sim Bd)$$

→2	Vd	
→3	$(x)(Vx \supset Hx)$	
4	$Vd \supset Hd$	3,UI
5	Hd	2,4,MP
6	$Bd \supset \sim Hd$	1,UI
7	$\sim Bd$	5,6,DN,MT
8	$(x)(Vx \supset Hx) \supset \sim Bd$	3–7,CP
9	$Vd \supset ((x)(Vx \supset Hx) \supset \sim Bd)$	2–9,CP

Here we have two applications of conditional proof, the first assumption being introduced at 2 and running to 8 and the second being introduced at 3 and running to 7. There is no objection to introducing as many assumptions as are found to be useful, *provided that* the scope of any later assumption falls *within* the scope of any earlier one. Suppose for example in a ten-line proof the scope of the first assumption runs from line 3 to line 7, the scope of the second must not run beyond line 6.

Exercises on Part IV

Translate the following arguments into logical symbolism and show that the conclusion follows validly from the premises:

1 Some vampires live in Transylvania. Anyone who lives in Transylvania lives in an iron curtain country. Any vampire who lives in an iron curtain country is classed as an anti-social hooligan. All those classed as anti-social hooligans are liable to be sent to a labour camp. *Therefore:* some vampires are liable to be sent to a labour camp.

2 All vampires and werewolves are bad neighbours. No bad neighbours are social workers or readers of the *Guardian*. Some werewolves are dangerous and underprivileged. Some vampires are not anti-social. All bad neighbours are antisocial. No underprivileged vampires read the *Guardian*. *Therefore:* some vampires are social workers.

3 All vampires come from central Europe and fly after dark. If anything flies after dark, it is either an owl or a bat or an aircraft. No vampires are owls or aircraft. All bats belong to the order Chiroptera. No vampires belong to the order Chiroptera. *Therefore:* There are no vampires.

4 All social workers or *Guardian* readers are virtuous. Some inconsiderate people read the *Guardian*. Some social workers are pretentious busybodies. No virtuous people are inconsiderate. Some social workers are philistines. *So:* some pretentious busybodies are philistines.

5 All warlocks are either native born or hold foreign passports. No native born warlock holds a foreign passport. Some warlocks hold a foreign passport. *Therefore:* some warlocks are not native born.

6 All warlocks and witches are either possessed by demons or on familiar terms with them. Anyone who is on familiar terms with demons is unfit to be a magistrate. Some magistrates are witches. No magistrate is possessed by demons. *Therefore:* some magistrates are unfit to be magistrates.

7 All vampires and werewolves despise social workers. Anyone who despises social workers is out of touch with modern progressive thought. No reader of the *Guardian* is out of touch with modern progressive thought. Vampires do exist. *Therefore:* No werewolf reads the *Guardian*.

8 All werewolves are affected by phases of the moon. Anyone who is affected by phases of the moon is an unstable per-

sonality and inefficient at his profession. Anyone who is not inefficient at his profession is respected by his neighbours. Anyone who has an unstable personality is in danger of falling into the hands of psychiatrists. No werewolf is in danger of falling into the hands of psychiatrists. *Therefore:* there are no werewolves.

9 Everything pleasant is either illegal, immoral or fattening. Eating chocolate is pleasant. Eating chocolate is neither illegal nor immoral. *Therefore:* eating chocolate is fattening.

10 If anyone holds a Transylvanian passport, he holds a forged passport and suffers from romantic nostalgia. Anyone who suffers from romantic nostalgia is oblivious to everyday reality. There is a holder of a Transylvanian passport who is not very rich. If anyone holds a forged passport, either he is very rich or he is in danger of trouble with immigration. If anyone is oblivious to everyday reality, either he is in danger of getting psychiatric help or he is very rich. *Therefore:* there is someone who is in danger both of getting psychiatric help and of trouble with immigration.

Part V

Looking Ahead

The methods that we have been studying enable us to deal with arguments at the truth-functional level and also with many arguments involving quantifiers. But there are still a great many arguments of a quite simple kind which the methods of the previous chapters cannot handle. There are two different but connected reasons for this. In some cases, we have not got sufficiently powerful techniques to enable us to prove the conclusions that we need. Moreover, we do not have an appropriate symbolism for formalising the premisses and conclusions of these arguments. These limitations go together because, as we have seen, methods of proof and ways of symbolising logical structures are closely connected.

Let us look at some examples of easy arguments which are still beyond the reach of the methods we have learned so far. We will do this simply in order to show the limitations of the elementary part of logic that we have been studying. This may encourage some readers to take their study of the subject further with the help of some of the books listed in the bibliography.

Consider first:

(A) Botticelli painted *La Primavera*.
Botticelli was Alessandro Filipepi.
So: Alessandro Filipepi painted *La Primavera*.

Writing 'P' for the predicate 'painted *La Primavera*' and '*b*' for the individual constant replacing 'Botticelli', we have the first premiss symbolised as:

$$Pb$$

But the second premiss says that the bearers of the two proper names 'Botticelli' and 'Alessandro Filipepi' are one and the same person. In other words, Botticelli is identical with Alessandro Filipepi. Now we have no means, in the logic so far available to us, of expressing the fact that two things or two people are identical. We can, of course, introduce a new symbol for this purpose. Let us say that 'A is identical' with 'B' is to be expressed in logic by 'A = B'. This is, in fact, the usual notation for identity in modern logic. We can then symbolise our argument as follows, using 'P' for 'painted *La Primavera*', '*b*' for 'Botticelli', '*f*' for 'Alessandro Filipepi' and '=' for 'is identical with'. We then have:

1 P*b*
2 *b* =
    Therefore: P*f*

And now we have to justify moving from the premises to the conclusion. This clearly requires a *rule* which tells us how to use our new symbol '=' just as earlier we needed rules to tell us how to use '⊃', '∨', '(∃x)' and the rest. And, in general, when the logically important features of natural language call for a symbolic notation, we must have rules to tell us how to use the new notation.

Here is another intuitively valid argument with which the logic we have learned so far does not equip us to deal.

(B) If London is larger than Bristol and Bristol is larger than Exeter, then London is larger than Exeter.

The validity of the argument clearly turns on some features of the predicate 'larger than'. We saw earlier, when we introduced the notion of a predicate, that is, a descriptive word or phrase, that some predicates can occur in meaningful sentences if they qualified only one individual. Others needed two or more individuals to qualify if they were to be used in a meaningful way. For example, we can say:

> The rose is red
> Tom is tall
> Sugar is sweet

and so on.

Words like 'red', 'tall' and 'sweet' can qualify a noun or a phrase referring to a single individual (or individuals). But we cannot say:

> The roses are between
> Tom is taller than
> Sugar is sweeter than

Such sentences need another noun or noun phrase to make sense. For example:

> The roses are between the path and the lupins
> Tom is taller than Bill
> Sugar is sweeter than sorbitol

We are dealing here with predicates that need two or more subjects. They are sometimes called two-place or three-place predicates to distinguish them from ordinary descriptive adjectives like 'hot' or 'green' which are one place predicates. And they are sometimes called 'relational predicates' because they refer to *relations* like 'larger than', 'equal to', 'between', 'to the north of' and so on. Relations have special logical properties and we have to spell out these properties and introduce a suitable symbolism for them if we are to handle even such simple arguments as B above. The symbolism is not particularly abstruse. Just as we can say:

Bj

for 'John has blue eyes' so we can say:

$$tLm \text{ or, more usually, } Ltm$$

for 'Tom loves Mary'. (And, conversely, we can write

$$Lmt$$

for 'Mary loves Tom'.) Here again we need rules to tell us
how to handle the new notation. And these rules (which we
shall not be dealing with here) will depend on the logical
properties of relations.

One consequence of these logical properties is that we
have to extend our rules for quantifiers by introducing two
or more sets of individuals governed by our quantifiers.
Suppose that we want to express in logical symbolism a
statement such as:

> There is an alligator in every swimming pool

This could be paraphrased as:

> For all x there is a y such that if x is a swimming pool
> then y is an alligator and y is in x

To symbolise this, we have to use two quantifiers with
different variables, thus:

$$(x)[(\exists y)Sx \supset (Ay . Iyx)]$$

We need these quantifiers if we are to express the logical structure of sentences containing relational predicates.
Here, the relational predicate is the two-termed predicate
'is in' symbolised by 'I'. (Note that the *order* in which the
quantified variables are attached to the predicate symbols is
important. 'Iyx' means 'y is in x'. 'Ixy' would make no sense
in this context.)

This notation can be used to extend the range of arguments which may seem 'intuitively' obvious but which cannot be dealt with by the methods of the previous chapters.
A simple example would be:

(C)   All alligators are reptiles
      Therefore: Whoever criticises an alligator criticises
      a reptile

Writing 'A' for 'is an alligator', 'R' for 'is a reptile' and 'Cxy' for 'x criticises y' we have:

$$(x)(Ax \supset Rx)$$
$$\therefore (x) [(\exists y)(Ay . Cxy) \supset (\exists y)(Ry . Cxy)]$$

Another transparently simple argument that requires quantification over more than one variable is:

(D) There is an alligator whom all crocodiles respect
  ∴ All crocodiles respect some alligator or other

This becomes:

$$(\exists y)[Ay . (x)(Cx \supset Rxy)]$$
$$\therefore (x)[Cx \supset (\exists y)(Ay . Rxy)]$$

Simple arguments such as C and D above can be shown to be valid once we have given them symbolic expression by adequate quantification. But many such arguments will need rules for dropping and restoring quantifiers a little more complex than the simplified rules that we have used in Part IV.

We have looked at a few of the types of argument with which the elementary logic of Parts I–IV does not deal. And there are, of course, still further ways of symbolising the logically important features of natural languages which cannot be dealt with in a short elementary book of this kind.

But there is another important set of questions that logicians ask which have not even been hinted at so far. These questions are not about arguments and the ways in which we formalise and validate them, but rather about the methods and techniques of logic itself. It will probably have occurred to some of you as you read the earlier parts of this book to ask: How do we know that these methods *always* give us the right answer? Can they not sometimes break down and lead us astray? Or how do we know that these methods are adequate to *all* the arguments that can be formulated in the symbolism that we have learned? Are all logically true statements provable?

Such questions are very basic and important. They concern some of the most profound issues with which logicians have dealt in the present century. But they are questions which concern not the effective application of logical techniques but with the very nature of logic itself. We can look very briefly and untechnically at three of these questions.

The first concerns *logical truths*. We saw in earlier chapters that one way of determining whether a particular expression is a logical truth is to construct its truth table. If the main column of the table gives nothing but 'true', then the expression is a logical truth. But how do we construct logical truths and what is the relation between them? Are some more basic than others? Questions of this sort have led logicians to the study of *systems of axioms*. Such systems have been an object of study by mathematicians since at least the fourth century BC when Euclid published his *Elements of Geometry*. If you open an edition of Euclid's *Elements* in the middle, you will find a proof of a proposition in geometry, say, that the sum of the internal angles of any triangle totals two right angles. This proof will be justified by reference to previous proofs, rather in the way that we have learned to justify proofs by our rules of inference. If we refer to these earlier proofs, we will be referred back to still earlier ones until in the end, we come to Euclid's starting point, a set of axioms. These he takes for granted as self evident and not requiring proof. (For example: things equal to the same thing are equal to one another.)

So, too, systems of logic start with axioms and rules of inference. These may or may not be 'self evident'. (Logicians and philosophers generally have learned to distrust self evidence as a sign of truth.) But such starting points for logic do have to conform to certain standards before they can be accepted as a reliable beginning for a system of logic.

The first of these standards is *consistency*. This is a fundamental concept in logic. And it is worth while asking the question: why do we need consistency in logic? The answer is that if a logical system is inconsistent, *anything whatever* can be proved in the system. And this, of course, takes the whole point out of logic which we need as a guide to true conclusions when we start from true premises. We saw earlier (on p. 128) that if we have an argument with two inconsistent or contradictory premises:

$$1 \quad P$$
$$2 \quad \sim P$$

we can prove Q where Q is *any proposition you like*. Thus:

$$3 \quad P \lor Q \qquad 1,\text{Add.}$$
$$4 \quad Q \qquad\quad 2,3,\text{DS}$$

So our logical system must be consistent if it is to be of any use at all.

The second property that logicians look for in a system of logic is a little more difficult to understand. It is called *completeness*. Suppose we ask of our original nineteen rules of inference: Are they complete? That is, do they enable us to prove *all* the logical truths of the logic of propositions? The answer is that, by themselves, they do not. If you doubt this, try to prove '(A ⊃ A)' from '(A ⊃ B)' using only the nineteen rules *without conditional proof*. Yet [(A ⊃ B) ⊃ (A ⊃ A)] is undoubtedly a logical truth. (Construct its truth table and see.) So clearly an incomplete system is, to some extent, an imperfect system (even if, for purposes of teaching, it is sometimes necessary to use it). And it is highly desirable to have a complete system of logic *if we can get it*.

But a proof that a logical system is complete is usually a complex and difficult one. Moreover, one of the most famous and important logical discoveries of this century was Gödel's proof, published in 1931, that all logical systems of more than a quite elementary kind must be incomplete. That is to say, we can always express, in such a system, a logical truth that cannot be proved in the system.

These two connected questions about axiom systems, that is, questions about their consistency and their completeness, are examples of the sort of questions that arise when we ask questions about logic itself. There are many more such questions; and the discussion and resolution of them constitutes an important part of contemporary research in logic. For it is important to realise that logic is not a dead and completed subject, as it was quite generally thought to be only fifty years ago. On the contrary, it is an extensive and growing area of scientific research and one of the most modern of the sciences. The chapters of this book are no more than an introduction to the very simplest parts of a large and important subject.

Solutions to Exercises

Part I

Chapter 1

1. (i) It will rain soon.
   (ii) Government revenues will not increase.
   (iii) Government revenues will not increase.
   (iv) The chief witness was not telling the truth.
2. (i) Arguments are valid.
   (ii) Statements are true.
3. (i), (ii), (iii), (iv), (viii), (ix) and (xii) are correct.
4. *Either:* If the evidence is forged, then the accused is guilty.
   The evidence is forged.
   Therefore: the accused is guilty.
   Or: If the accused is guilty, then the evidence is forged.
   The accused is guilty.
   Therefore: the evidence is forged.
5. (i)

Chapter 2

1. (a) (i) The sun shines. The corn ripens.
   (xvi) Atomic power can be widely applied in industry. Coal mining will lose its importance.
   (xvii) England lose the test match. The team will be changed.

(b) (iv)   He has enough money. He will buy a book and a record.

(vii)   Inflation continues. The standard of living will not rise.

(x)   Jones comes. Smith will come and Robinson will stay away.

(xiii)   The play is good. The run will not be a short one.

(xix)   Public spending is increased. Inflation will accelerate and taxes will not be cut.

(xx)   Smith comes. Jones will come and Robinson will not come.

(c) (v)   The car does not start. We shall go by train.

(xi)   The play is good and the acting is competent. The author will make money.

(xii)   The play is not good. The run will be a short one.

(xviii)   The team is not changed. England win the test match.

(d) (viii)   It does not rain. The grass will not be wet and the match will not be abandoned.

2 (a) (ii)   The day is bright. The day is sunny.

  (b) (iii)   He bought a record. He did not buy a book.

  (c) (vi)   Jones did not come. The meeting was postponed.

     (xv)   The summer was not wet. The harvest was good.

3 (a) (v)   The car starts. (S)

     (vii)   The standard of living will rise. (S)

     (ix)   It is wet and stormy. (C)

     (xii)   The play is good. (S)

     (xiv)   The play will be good and the run will be short. (C)

     (xx)   Robinson will come. (S)

4   (i) $S \supset C$

    (ii) $B . S$

    (iii) $R . \sim B$

    (v) $\sim C \supset T$

    (vi) $\sim J . M$

    (vii) $I \supset \sim S$

    (xii) $\sim P \supset R$

    (xiii) $P \supset \sim R$

    (xv) $\sim S . H$

    (xvi) $A \supset C$

    (xvii) $E \supset T$

    (xviii) $\sim T \supset E$

5   (i), (xvi), (xvii) have the same form: $(p \supset q)$

(v), (xi), (xviii) have the form: $(\sim p \supset q)$
(vi), (xv) have the same form: $(\sim p \cdot q)$
(vii), (xiii) have the same form: $(p \supset \sim q)$

Chapter 3   page 32
1   0, 1
2   1, 1
3   0, 0
4   0, 1
5   0, 1
6   (a) $p \not\supset q$
    (b) $\sim p \supset q$
    (c) $p \cdot q$
    (d) $\sim(p \cdot q)$
    (e) $\sim p \cdot \sim q$
    (f) $\sim p \cdot q$
    (g) $p \supset \sim q$
7   (a) Contradiction
    (b) Contingent statement
    (c) Contingent statement
    (d) Logical truth
    (e) Contingent statement

Chapter 4   page 39
1   (a) C . F
    (b) C ⊃ F
    (c) F ⊃ C
    (d) F . C
2   (a) Alfred burned the cakes and Boadicea was Queen of the
        Iceni.
    (b) Boadicea was Queen of the Iceni and Alfred burned the
        cakes.
    (c) If Boadicea was Queen of the Iceni, then Alfred burned
        the cakes.
    (d) If Alfred burned the cakes, then Boadicea was Queen of
        the Iceni.
    (e) Alfred burned the cakes but Boadicea was not Queen of
        the Iceni.
    (f) It is false that Alfred burned the cakes and Boadicea was
        Queen of the Iceni.
    (g) If Alfred did not burn the cakes, then Boadicea was
        Queen of the Iceni.

3 (i) 1a   (ii) 1b
      1d   1c
      2a   2c
      2b   2d

4 Yes. The definition of the conjunction sign gives the rules for assigning truth values to the conjunction of any two propositions whatsoever.

5 (a) 1000
   (b) 0010
   (c) 0100
   (d) 0111
   (e) 1101
   (f) 0111

6   R . ~R
   1 0   01
   0 0   10

Chapter 5   page 43

1 p and q; r and s. Dot sign.
2 $(p . r)$ and $(r . s)$ Hook sign.
3 $(s \supset t)$ and $(t \supset r)$ Third occurrence of the hook sign.
4 r and w Hook sign.
5 $(p \supset q)$ and $[(w \supset r) . (q \supset w)]$
   First occurrence of the dot sign.
6 Third occurrence of the dot sign.
   $[(s \supset t) . (t \supset r)]$ and $(p \supset q)$
   $(s \supset t)$ and $(t \supset r)$
7 (a) 1 $(p \supset q)$ and $(r \supset s)$
       5   $(p \supset q)$ and $[(w \supset r) . (q \supset w)]$
       6   $\{[(s \supset t) . (t \supset r)] . (p \supset q)\}$ and
           $[(p \supset q) . (r \supset s)]$
   (b) 2 $(p . r)$; $(r . s)$
       3   $[(s \supset t) . (t \supset r)]$; $(s \supset r)$
       4   $[(s \supset t) . (t \supset r)]$; $[(s \supset r) . (r . w)]$

Chapter 6   page 46

(A) 1 p
    2   $p . q$
    3   q
    4   $p . q$
    5   $(p . q) \supset (r . s)$

6 First occurrence: $\sim(r \cdot s) \cdot (t \supset u)$
  Second occurrence: $r \cdot s$
7 p, q
8 $r \supset s; t \cdot u$
9 $r \supset s; t$

(B) 1 $\supset$
  2 $\sim$
  3 $\supset$
  4 $\supset$
  5 $\sim$
  6 $\sim$
  7 $\cdot$
  8 $\supset$
  9 $\supset$

Chapter 7   *page 52*

1   $\sim p \supset q$
   0 1 1 1
   0 1 1 0
   1 0 1 1
   1 0 0 0

2   $\sim(p \cdot q)$
   0 1 11
   1 1 00
   1 0 01
   1 0 00

3   $p \supset \sim q$
   1 0 0 1
   1 1 1 0
   0 1 0 1
   0 1 1 0

4   $\sim p \cdot \sim q$
   0 1 0 0 1
   0 1 0 1 0
   1 0 0 0 1
   1 0 1 1 0

5 $(p \supset q) . (\sim q \supset p)$
   1 1 1 1 0 1 1 1
   1 0 0 0 1 0 1 1
   0 1 1 1 0 1 1 0
   0 1 0 0 1 0 0 0

6 $(\sim p . q) \supset (p \supset \sim q)$
   0 1 0 1 1 1 1 0 1
   0 1 0 0 1 1 0 1 0
   1 0 1 1 1 0 1 0 1
   1 0 0 0 1 0 1 1 0

7 $\sim(\sim p \supset q) . \sim(p \supset \sim q)$
   0 0 1 1 1 0 1 1 0 0 1
   0 0 1 1 0 0 0 1 1 1 0
   0 1 0 1 1 0 0 0 1 0 1
   1 1 0 0 0 0 0 0 1 1 0

8 $\sim[(\sim p . \sim q) \supset (q \supset p)]$
   0 0 1 0 0 1 1 1 1 1
   0 0 1 0 1 0 1 0 1 1
   0 1 0 0 0 1 1 1 0 0
   0 1 0 1 1 0 1 0 1 0

9 $\sim[(p \supset q) \supset (\sim q \supset \sim p)]$
   0 1 1 1 1 0 1 1 0 1
   0 1 0 0 1 1 0 0 0 1
   0 0 1 1 1 0 1 1 1 0
   0 0 1 0 1 1 0 1 1 0

10 $\sim[\sim(\sim p . q) \supset (\sim q . \sim p)]$
   1 1 0 1 0 1 0 0 1 0 0 1
   1 1 0 1 0 0 0 1 0 0 0 1
   0 0 1 0 1 1 1 0 1 0 1 0
   0 1 1 0 0 0 1 1 0 1 1 0

Chapter 8   *page 55*

1 $(p . q) \supset (q . r)$
   1 1 1 1 1 1 1
   1 1 1 0 1 0 0
   1 0 0 1 0 0 1
   1 0 0 1 0 0 0
   0 0 1 1 1 1 1
   0 0 1 1 1 0 0
   0 0 0 1 0 0 1
   0 0 0 1 0 0 0

2 $(\sim p \cdot q) \supset (\sim q \cdot r)$

```
01 01  1   01 01
01 01  1   01 00
01 00  1   10 11
01 00  1   10 00
10 11  0   01 01
10 11  0   01 00
10 00  1   10 11
10 00  1   10 00
```

3 $\sim(p \supset q) \supset (q \cdot r)$

```
0 11  1 1   1 11
0 11  1 1   1 00
1 10  0 0   0 01
1 10  0 0   0 00
0 01  1 1   1 11
0 01  1 1   1 00
0 01  0 1   0 01
0 01  0 1   0 00
```

4 $[(p \supset q) \supset r] \supset [(p \cdot q) \supset r]$

```
1 1  1  1 1   1 11  1  1
1 1  1  0 0 1   1 11  0  0
1 0  0  1 1 1   1 00  1  1
1 0  0  1 0 1   1 00  1  0
0 1  1  1 1 1   0 01  1  1
0 1  1  0 0 1   0 01  1  0
0 1  0  1 1 1   0 00  1  1
0 1  0  0 0 1   0 00  1  0
```

5 $[(\sim p \supset \sim q) \supset r] \supset [\sim r \supset (p \cdot q)]$

```
0 11  01 1  1 1   0 11  1 11
0 11  01 0  0 1   1 01  1 11
0 11  10 1  1 1   0 11  1 00
0 11  10 0  0 1   1 00  1 00
1 00  01 1  1 1   0 11  0 01
1 00  01 1  0 0   1 00  0 01
1 01  10 1  1 1   0 01  0 00
1 01  10 0  0 1   1 00  0 00
```

6   [(p ⊃ q) . (q ⊃ r)] ⊃ (p ⊃ r)

```
1 1 1 1 1 1 1 1 1 1 1
1 1 1 0 1 0 0 1 1 0 0
1 0 0 0 0 1 1 1 1 1 1
1 0 0 0 0 1 0 1 1 0 0
0 1 1 1 1 1 1 1 0 1 1
0 1 1 0 1 0 0 1 0 1 0
0 1 0 1 0 1 1 1 0 1 1
0 1 0 1 0 1 0 1 0 1 0
```

7   [(~p . q) ⊃ ~r] ⊃ [(r . ~q) ⊃ ~p]

```
0 1 01 1 01 1    1 0 01 1 01
0 1 01 1 10 1    0 0 01 1 01
0 1 00 1 01 0    1 1 10 0 01
0 1 00 1 10 1    0 0 10 1 01
1 0 11 0 01 1    1 0 01 1 10
1 0 11 1 10 1    0 0 01 1 10
1 0 00 1 01 1    1 1 10 1 10
1 0 00 1 10 1    0 0 10 1 10
```

8   [(p ⊃ r) ⊃ (~r ⊃ ~p)] ⊃ (p ⊃ p)

```
1 1 1 1   011 01 1   1 1 1
1 0 0 1   100 01 1   1 1 1
1 1 1 1   011 01 1   1 1 1
1 0 0 1   100 01 1   1 1 1
0 1 1 1   011 10 1   0 1 0
0 1 0 1   101 10 1   0 1 0
0 1 1 1   011 10 1   0 1 0
0 1 0 1   101 10 1   0 1 0
```

9   [(p ⊃ r) . (~q ⊃ ~r)] ⊃ (~q ⊃ ~p)

```
1 1 1 1 011 01 1   011 01
1 0 0 0 011 10 1   011 01
1 1 1 0 100 01 1   100 01
1 0 0 0 101 10 1   100 01
0 1 1 1 011 01 1   011 10
0 1 0 1 011 10 1   011 10
0 1 1 0 100 01 1   101 10
0 1 0 1 101 10 1   101 10
```

10   [(p . r) ⊃ ~q] ⊃ [q ⊃ ~(p . r)]

```
111 0 01 1   10 0 111
100 1 01 1   11 1 100
```

```
1 11 1  10 1  01  0 1 11
1 00 1  10 1  01  1 1 00
0 01 1  01 1  11  1 0 01
0 00 1  01 1  11  1 0 00
0 01 1  10 1  01  1 0 01
0 00 1  10 1  01  1 0 00
```

Chapter 9   *page 59*
1   [(S ⊃ J) . S] ⊃ J
2   [(B ⊃ M) . B] ⊃ M
3   (J ⊃ S) . (S ⊃ J)
4   R . B
5   ~(R . B)
6   R . ~B
7   ~(A ⊃ C)
8   (C ⊃ G) . G
9   (C ⊃ G) . ~G
10 [(C ⊃ G) . ~G] ⊃ ~C
11 [(R ⊃ D) . ~D] ⊃ ~R
12 ~E . ~B
13 (E . B) ⊃ P
14 ~B ⊃ (~W . M)
15 (M ⊃ H) . (~M ⊃ S)

Chapter 10   *page 64*
1   [(C ⊃ K) . C] ⊃ K
    1 1 1 11 1 1
    1 0 0 01 1 0
    0 1 1 00 1 1
    0 1 0 00 1 0 Valid

2   [(W ⊃ B) . ~W] ⊃ ~B
    1 1 1 001 1 01
    1 0 0 001 1 10
    0 1 1 110 0 01
    0 1 0 110 1 10 Invalid

3   [(W ⊃ B) . ~B] ⊃ ~W
    1 1 1 001 1 01
    1 0 0 010 1 01
    0 1 1 001 1 10
    0 1 0 110 1 10 Valid
```
```

4 [(R ⊃ P) . P] ⊃ R
   1 1 1 11 1 1
   1 0 0 00 1 1
   0 1 1 11 0 0
   0 1 0 00 1 0 Invalid

5 (L . B) ⊃ L
   1 11 1 1
   1 00 1 1
   0 01 1 0
   0 00 1 0 Valid

6 L ⊃ (L . B)
   1 1 1 11
   1 0 1 00
   0 1 0 01
   0 1 0 00 Invalid

7 [(C ⊃ G) . ~G] ⊃ ~C
   1 1 1 001 1 01
   1 0 0 010 1 01
   0 1 1 001 1 10
   0 1 0 110 1 10 Valid

8 [(A ⊃ I) . (I ⊃ T)] ⊃ (A ⊃ T)
   1 1 1 1 11 1 1 1 1 1
   1 1 1 0 10 0 1 1 0 0
   1 0 0 0 01 1 1 1 1 1
   1 0 0 0 01 0 1 1 0 0
   0 1 1 1 11 1 1 0 1 1
   0 1 1 0 10 0 1 0 1 0
   0 1 0 1 01 1 1 0 1 1
   0 1 0 1 01 0 1 0 1 0 Valid

9 (I ⊃ T) ⊃ (~T ⊃ ~I)
   11 1 1 01 1 01
   10 0 1 10 0 01
   01 1 1 01 1 10
   01 0 1 10 1 10 Valid

10 {[(A ⊃ I) . (I ⊃ T)] . A} ⊃ T
   1 1 1 11 1 1 11 1 1
   1 1 1 01 0 0 01 1 0
   1 0 0 01 1 1 01 1 1
   1 0 0 01 0 0 01 1 0

```
0  1  1  1  1  1  1    00    1  1
0  1  1  0  1  0  0    00    1  0
0  1  0  1  0  1  1    00    1  1
0  1  0  1  0  1  0    00    1  0   Valid
```

11   [(A ⊃ C) . (C ⊃ F)] ⊃ (~F ⊃ ~A)

```
1  1  1   1  1  1   1   1   0 1 1   0 1
1  1  1   0  1  0  0   1   1 0 0   0 1
1  0  0   0  0  1   1   1   0 1 1   0 1
1  0  0   0  0  1  0   1   1 0 0   0 1
0  1  1   1  1  1   1   1   0 1 1   1 0
0  1  1   0  1  0  0   1   1 0 1   1 0
0  1  0   1  0  1   1   1   0 1 1   1 0
0  1  0   1  0  1  0   1   1 0 1   1 0   Valid
```

12   [(E . B) ⊃ ~G] ⊃ [G ⊃ ~(E . B)]

```
1 11  0  01  1   1  0  0 1 1 1
1 11  1  10  1   0  1  0 1 1 1
1 00  1  01  1   1  1  1 1 0 0
1 00  1  10  1   0  1  1 1 0 0
0 01  1  01  1   1  1  1 0 0 1
0 01  1  10  1   0  1  1 0 0 1
0 00  1  01  1   1  1  1 0 0 0
0 00  1  10  1   0  1  1 0 0 0   Valid
```

13   {[(E ⊃ B) . (B ⊃ P)] . ~P} ⊃ ~E

```
1  1  1   1  1  1   1   001   1   0 1
1  1  1   0  1  0  0   010   1   0 1
1  0  0   0  0  1   1   001   1   0 1
1  0  0   0  0  1  0   010   1   0 1
0  1  1   1  1  1   1   001   1   1 0
0  1  1   0  1  0  0   010   1   1 0
0  1  0   1  0  1   1   001   1   1 0
0  1  0   1  0  1  0   110   1   1 0   Valid
```

14   [(~F ⊃ V) . (~P ⊃ ~V)] ⊃ (~P ⊃ F)

```
0 1 1  1  1 0 1 1   01   1   0 1 1  1
0 1 1  1  0 1 0 0   01   1   1 0 1  1
0 1 1  0  1 0 1 1   10   1   0 1 1  1
0 1 1  0  1 1 0 1   10   1   1 0 1  1
1 0 1  1  1 0 1 1   01   1   0 1 1  0
1 0 1  1  0 1 0 0   01   1   1 0 0  0
1 0 0  0  0 0 1 1   10   1   0 1 1  0
1 0 0  0  0 1 0 1   10   1   1 0 0  0   Valid
```

15 $[E \supset (L . G) . \sim G] \supset \sim E$

1 1	1 11	001	1	01
1 0	1 00	010	1	01
1 0	0 01	001	1	01
1 0	0 00	010	1	01
0 1	1 11	001	1	10
0 1	1 00	110	1	10
0 1	0 01	001	1	10
0 1	0 00	110	1	10	Valid

Chapter 12 *page 76*

1   $W \supset R$
2   $E \supset \sim W$
3   $\sim W \supset \sim P$
4   $M \vee E$
5   $E \equiv \sim W$
6   $S \vee J$
7   $(P . \sim R) \vee (R . \sim P)$
8   $M . J$
9   $J . M$
10 $L . N$
11 'larger than' is a relation.
12 $J . N$
13 'brother of' is a relation.
14 $P \supset W$
15 $P \supset G$
16 $S \vee F$
17 $\sim R \supset H$
18 $R \vee H$
19 $\sim H \equiv R$
20 $\sim N \supset E$
21 $\sim E \supset N$
22 $N \supset (\sim E . S)$
23 $A \supset (S . L)$
24 $(S . L) \supset A$
25 $A \equiv (S . L)$
26 $\sim A \vee L$
27 $\sim P \vee (N . R)$
28 $P \supset (N \supset R)$
29 $F \supset (P . D)$
30 $\sim F \vee (P \supset I)$

(A) 1 $(p \supset q) \equiv \sim(p \cdot \sim q)$
    1 1 1 1 1 1 0 0 1
    1 0 0 1 0 1 1 1 0
    0 1 1 1 1 0 0 0 1
    0 1 0 1 1 0 0 1 0

                        Logically equivalent

  2   $\sim(p \vee q) \equiv (p \supset q)$
    0 1 1 1 0 1 1 1
    0 1 1 0 1 1 0 0
    0 0 1 1 0 0 1 1
    1 0 0 0 1 0 1 0

                        Not logically equivalent

  3   $(p \cdot q) \equiv \sim(\sim p \vee \sim q)$
    1 11 1 1 0 1 0 0 1
    1 00 1 0 0 1 1 1 0
    0 01 1 0 1 0 1 0 1
    0 00 1 0 1 0 1 1 0

                        Logically equivalent

  4   $(p \cdot q) \equiv \sim(p \supset \sim q)$
    1 11 1 1 1 0 0 1
    1 00 1 0 1 1 1 0
    0 01 1 0 0 1 0 1
    0 00 1 0 0 1 1 0

                        Logically equivalent

  5   $(p \vee q) \equiv (\sim p \supset q)$
    1 1 1 1 0 1 1 1
    1 1 0 1 0 1 1 0
    0 1 1 1 1 0 1 1
    0 0 0 1 1 0 0 0

                        Logically equivalent

  6   $(p \supset q) \equiv (q \supset p)$
    1 1 1 1 1 1 1
    1 0 0 0 0 1 1
    0 1 1 0 1 0 0
    0 1 0 1 0 1 0

                        Not logically equivalent

7 $(p \supset q) \equiv (\sim q \supset \sim p)$
   1 1 1 1   0 1 1 0 1
   1 0 0 1   1 0 0 0 1
   0 1 1 1   0 1 1 1 0
   0 1 0 1   1 0 1 1 0

                             Logically equivalent

8 $(p \lor q) \equiv \sim(\sim p \mathbin{.} \sim q)$
   1 1 1 1 1 0 1 0 0 1
   1 1 0 1 1 0 1 0 1 0
   0 1 1 1 1 1 0 0 0 1
   0 0 0 1 0 1 0 1 1 0

                             Logically equivalent

9 $\sim(p \mathbin{.} q) \equiv (\sim p \lor \sim q)$
   0 1 1 1 1   0 1 0 0 1
   1 1 0 0 1   0 1 1 1 0
   1 0 0 1 1   1 0 1 0 1
   1 0 0 0 1   1 0 1 1 0

                             Logically equivalent

10 $(p \mathbin{.} q) \equiv (\sim p \mathbin{.} \sim q)$
    1 1 1 0 0 1 0 0 1
    1 0 0 1 0 1 0 1 0
    0 0 1 1 1 0 0 0 1
    0 0 0 0 1 0 1 1 0

                         Not logically equivalent

11 $\{[(p \mathbin{.} q) \mathbin{.} (\sim p \mathbin{.} q)] \mathbin{.} (p \mathbin{.} \sim q)\} \equiv (p \lor q)$
    1 1 1 0 0 1 0 1 0 1 0 0 1 0 1 1 1
    1 0 0 0 0 1 0 0 0 1 1 1 0 0 1 1 0
    0 0 1 0 1 0 1 1 0 0 0 0 1 0 0 1 1
    0 0 0 0 1 0 0 0 0 0 0 1 0 1 0 0 0

                             Not logically equivalent

12 $(p \equiv q) \equiv [(p \mathbin{.} q) \lor (\sim p \mathbin{.} \sim q)]$
   1 1 1 1   1 1 1 1 0 1 0 0 1
   1 0 0 1   1 0 0 0 0 1 0 1 0
   0 0 1 1   0 0 1 0 1 0 0 0 1
   0 1 0 1   0 0 0 1 1 0 1 1 0

                             Logically equivalent

(B)   R ⊃ H
   1 ~H ⊃ ~R
   2 ~R ∨ ~H
   3 H ∨ ~R
   4 ~(H . ~R)

Of these, 1 and 3 are logically equivalent to R ⊃ H.

  1 (R ⊃ H) ≡ (~H ⊃ ~R)
     1 1 1 1 0 1 1 0 1
     1 0 0 1 1 0 0 0 1
     0 1 1 1 0 1 1 1 0
     0 1 0 1 1 0 1 1 0

  2 (R ⊃ H) ≡ (~R ∨ ~H)
     1 1 1 0 0 1 0 0 1
     1 0 0 0 0 1 1 1 0
     0 1 1 1 1 0 1 0 1
     0 1 0 1 1 0 1 1 0

                                    Not logically equivalent

  3 (R ⊃ H) ≡ (H ∨ ~R)
     1 1 1 1 1 1 0 1
     1 0 0 1 0 0 0 1
     0 1 1 1 1 1 1 0
     0 1 0 1 0 1 1 0

  4 (R ⊃ H) ≡ ~(H . ~R)
     1 1 1 1 1 1 0 0 1
     1 0 0 0 1 0 0 0 1
     0 1 1 0 0 1 1 1 0
     0 1 0 1 1 0 0 1 0

                                    Not logically equivalent

(C)   (A . H) ⊃ S
   1 ~S ⊃ ~(A ∨ H)
   2 ~H ⊃ (~S ⊃ ~A)
   3 ~S ⊃ (A . ~H)
   4 (~S . A) ⊃ ~H
   5 ~S ⊃ (~A ∨ ~H)
   6 A ⊃ (H ⊃ S)

Of these, 4, 5 and 6 are logically equivalent to (A . H) ⊃ S and, therefore, logically equivalent to each other.

```
      (A . H) ⊃ S
      1 11  1  1
      1 11  0  0
      1 00  1  1
      1 00  1  0
      0 01  1  1
      0 01  1  0
      0 00  1  1
      0 00  1  0
```

The main column gives: **1 0 1 1 1 1 1 1**

```
1   [(A . H)  ⊃  S]  ≡  [∼S  ⊃  ∼(A ∨ H)]
         1     1      0 1 1    0 1 1 1
         0     1      1 0 0    0 1 1 1
         1     1      0 1 1    0 1 1 0
         1     0      1 0 0    0 1 1 0
         1     1      0 1 1    0 0 1 1
         1     0      1 0 0    0 0 1 1
         1     1      0 1 1    1 0 0 0
         1     1      1 0 1    1 0 0 0
```
                                    Not logically equivalent

```
2   [(A . H)  ⊃  S]  ≡  [∼H  ⊃  (∼S  ⊃  ∼A)]
         1     1      0 1 1     0 1 1  0 1
         0     0      0 1 1     1 0 0  0 1
         1     1      1 0 1     0 1 1  0 1
         1     0      1 0 0     1 0 0  0 1
         1     1      0 1 1     0 1 1  1 0
         1     1      0 1 1     1 0 1  1 0
         1     1      1 0 1     0 1 1  1 0
         1     1      1 0 1     1 0 1  1 0
```
                                    Not logically equivalent

```
3   [(A . H)  ⊃  S]  ≡  [∼S  ⊃  (A . ∼H)]
         1     1      0 1 1     1 0 0 1
         0     1      1 0 0     1 0 0 1
         1     1      0 1 1     1 1 1 0
         1     1      1 0 1     1 1 1 0
         1     1      0 1 1     0 0 0 1
         1     0      1 0 0     0 0 0 1
         1     1      0 1 1     0 0 1 0
         1     0      1 0 0     0 0 1 0
```
                                    Not logically equivalent

4 [(A . H) ⊃ S] ≡ [(∼S . A) ⊃ ∼H]
        1   1   01 01 1 01
        0   1   10 11 0 01
        1   1   01 01 1 10
        1   1   10 11 1 10
        1   1   01 00 1 01
        1   1   10 00 1 01
        1   1   01 00 1 10
        1   1   10 00 1 10
                    Logically equivalent

5 [(A . H) ⊃ S] ≡ [∼S ⊃ (∼A ∨ ∼H)]
        1   1   01 1   01 0 01
        0   1   10 0   01 0 01
        1   1   01 1   01 1 10
        1   1   10 1   01 1 10
        1   1   01 1   10 1 01
        1   1   10 1   10 1 01
        1   1   01 1   10 1 10
        1   1   10 1   10 1 10
                    Logically equivalent

6 [(A . H) ⊃ S] ≡ [A ⊃ (H ⊃ S)]
        1   1   1 1   1 1 1
        0   0   1 0   1 0 0
        1   1   1 1   0 1 1
        1   1   1 1   0 1 0
        1   1   0 1   1 1 1
        1   1   0 1   1 0 0
        1   1   0 1   0 1 1
        1   1   0 1   0 1 0
                    Logically equivalent

Chapter 14   *page 89*

1 Invalid
2 Valid
3 Valid
4 Invalid
5 Valid
6 Valid
7 Invalid
8 Valid

 9 Valid
10 Valid
11 Invalid
12 Valid

Important Note: As the shorter truth-table method is not a mechanical procedure, more than one way is normally available to show that a particular form is invalid or valid. We have therefore not given solutions to all the examples since, if we did so, it is unlikely that your workings, even though correct, would be the same as ours.

Sample workings of 1, 7 and 12 are given below:

1 (A ∨ B) . A ⊃ B

1	1	1	1	1	0	0

  5   3 6 1 4   2

Invalid

2 [(Q ⊃ P) . (R ⊃ Ṗ)] ⊃ (Q ⊃ R)

1	1	1	1	0	1	1	0	1	0	0

7   3   8 1 9   4 10   5 2 6

Invalid

3 {[(A ∨ B) ⊃ C] . [(C ∨ D) ⊃ E]} ⊃ (B ⊃ E)

	1	1	1	1	1	1	1		1	0	0	1	0	0

    9 7 3 10 1   11 12   4 8   5 2 6

Valid

Rule violated by steps 12, 4 and 8 together.

 1 Valid
 2 Valid

3	Invalid
4	Valid
5	Valid
6	Valid
7	Valid
8	Invalid
9	Valid
10	Invalid
11	Valid
12	Valid

Exercises on Part 1   *page 98*

(A)	1	Valid
	2	Valid
	3	Valid
	4	Valid
	5	Valid
	6	Invalid
	7	Valid
	8	Invalid
	9	Invalid
	10	Invalid
	11	Valid
	12	Valid
	13	Invalid
	14	Valid
	15	Valid
	16	Invalid
	17	Valid
	18	Invalid
	19	Valid
	20	Valid
	21	Valid
	22	Valid
	23	Valid
	24	Valid
	25	Valid
	26	Invalid
	27	Valid
	28	Valid
	29	Valid
	30	Valid

31 Valid
32 Valid
33 Valid
34 Valid
35 Logically equivalent
36 Logically equivalent
37 Valid
38 Valid
39 Logically equivalent
40 Logically equivalent
41 Logically equivalent
42 Logically equivalent
43 Logically equivalent
44 Logically equivalent

(B) 1 [(G ∨ F) . (~B ⊃ ~F) . (B ⊃ R)] ⊃ (~R ⊃ G)
   Valid

 2 {[(R . E) ⊃ (O . I)] . (E ⊃ ~I)} ⊃ (~E ∨ ~R)
   Valid

 3 {[(A . P) ⊃ S] . [S ⊃ (C . O)] . ~O} ⊃ (A ⊃ ~P)
   Valid

 4 [(C ∨ H) . (C ⊃ T) . (T ⊃ ~A) . (A ∨ O)] ⊃ O
   Invalid

 5 {[~(P . ~R) ⊃ I] . (I ⊃ F) . ~F} ⊃ ~(~P ∨ R)
   Valid

 6 [(A ⊃ ~B) . (~B ⊃ C)] ⊃ (~C ⊃ ~A)
   Valid

 7 [(G ⊃ C) . (I ⊃ ~C) . I] ⊃ ~G
   Valid

 8 {{A ⊃ [C ⊃ (D . W)]} . (C . ~D)} ⊃ ~A
   Valid

 9 [(~F ⊃ V) . ~(F ∨ ~S) . (~P ⊃ ~S)] ⊃ (V . P)
   Valid

10 {[(P . L) ⊃ R] . (R ⊃ D) . ~D} ⊃ (P ⊃ ~L)
   Valid

11 [(J ∨ P) ⊃ (B ∨ ~R)] ⊃ [(R ∨ P) ⊃ (J ⊃ B)]
   Invalid

12 [J ⊃ S) . (B ⊃ ~S) . (J ⊃ ~E)] ⊃ S
   Invalid

13 [(J ⊃ S) . (B ⊃ ~S)] ⊃ (J ⊃ ~B)
   Valid

14 {[(G ∨ F) ⊃ (J ∨ S)] . [(F ∨ J) ⊃ P] . ∼P . G} ⊃ S
                                             Valid

15 {[(G ∨ F) ⊃ (J ∨ S)] . [(J ∨ F) ⊃ P] . (G ⊃ P) . ∼P}
    ⊃ (J ∨ S)   Invalid

16 [(E ⊃ ∼P) . (∼P ∨ C) . ∼C] ⊃ (∼E ∨ A)
                                         Invalid

17 {[P ⊃ (R ⊃ S)] . (∼R ⊃ H) . (∼S . ∼H) . P} ⊃ E
                                         Valid

18 [D ⊃ (S ⊃ M) . (∼R ∨ D) . S] ⊃ (R ⊃ M)
                                         Valid

19 {[(F ∨ P) ⊃ ∼G] . (∼T ⊃ F) . (T ⊃ G) . ∼F} ⊃ ∼P
                                         Valid

Part II

Section 1   *page 106*

  2 Addition
  3 Destructive Dilemma
  4 Hypothetical Syllogism
  5 Modus Tollens
  6 Constructive Dilemma
  7 Conjunction
  8 Disjunctive Syllogism
  9 Simplification
10 Modus Tollens

Section 2   *page 108*

1 Disjunctive Syllogism
2 Simplification
3 Addition
4 3∼ (V ∨ W) Modus Tollens
5 3. C ∨ L Constructive Dilemma
6 3. F . G Modus Ponens
7 Destructive Dilemma
8 3. L ⊃ P Hypothetical Syllogism
9 3, Conjunction

1   (1) T . S   /∴ T ∨ U
    (2) T   1,Simp.
    (3) T ∨ U   2,Add.
2   (1) (J ⊃ K) . (L ⊃ M)
    (2) J   /∴ K ∨ M
    (3) J ∨ L   2,Add.
    (4) K ∨ M   1,3,CD
3   (1) A ⊃ B
    (2) C ⊃ D
    (3) ~B ∨ ~D   /∴ ~A ∨ ~C
    (4) (A ⊃ B) . (C ⊃ D)   1,2,Conj.
    (5) ~A ∨ ~C   3,4,DD
4   (1) (D ∨ S) . (F ⊃ G)
    (2) ~D   /∴ S
    (3) D ∨ S   1,Simp.
    (4) S   3,2,DS
5   (1) (A ⊃ B) ∨ (L ⊃ H)
    (2) ~(A ⊃ B)
    (3) L   /∴ H
    (4) L ⊃ H   1,2,DS
    (5) H   2,3,4,MP
6   (1) (P ⊃ Q) . (R ⊃ S)
    (2) ~Q   /∴ ~P
    (3) P ⊃ Q   1,Simp.
    (4) ~P   3,4,MT
7   (1) [P ⊃ (Q . R)] . [(Q . R) ⊃ S]
    (2) ~S   /∴ ~P
    (3) P ⊃ S   1,HS
    (4) ~P   3,2,MT
8   (1) [(F ∨ ~J) ⊃ (P . M)] . [(B . V) ⊃ (K . Q)]
    (2) ~(P . M)
    (3) (F ∨ ~J) ∨ (B . V)   /∴ K . Q
    (4) (P . M) ∨ (K . Q)   1,3,CD
    (5) K . Q   4,2,DS
9   (1) [(Z ∨ S) ⊃ (T . Y)] . [(M ∨ N) ⊃ (O . P)]
    (2) Q
    (3) ~(T . Y) ∨ ~(O . P)   /∴ [~(Z∨S)∨~(M∨N)] . Q
    (4) ~(Z ∨ S) ∨ ~(M ∨ N)
                                     1,3,DD
    (5) [~(Z ∨ S) ∨ ~(M ∨ N)] . Q
                                     4,2,Conj.

10   (1) [J ∨ (V ⊃ Z)] ⊃ (~P ∨ T)
     (2) J   /∴ ~P ∨ T
     (3) J ∨ (V ⊃ Z)   2,Add.
     (4) ~P ∨ T   1,3,MP

Section 4   *page 111*

1   (1) (A ⊃ S) . (B ⊃ F)
    (2) (A ∨ B)
    (3) (S ⊃ B) . (F ⊃ W)   /∴ B ∨ W
    (4) S ∨ F   1,2,CD
    (5) B ∨ W   3,4,CD

2   (1) (R ⊃ P) . (P ⊃ ~L)
    (2) T ⊃ L
    (3) R ∨ T   /∴ P ∨ L
    (4) R ⊃ P   1,Simp.
    (5) (R ⊃ P) . (T ⊃ L)   4,2,Conj.
    (6) P ∨ L   5,3,CD

3   (1) (A ∨ G) ⊃ S
    (2) A . T   /∴ S
    (3) A   2,Simp.
    (4) A ∨ G   3,Add.
    (5) S   1,4,MP

4   (1) A ∨ ~I
    (2) D ⊃ I
    (3) ~A
    (4) (~D . ~I) ⊃ W   /∴ W
    (5) ~I   1,3,DS
    (6) ~D   2,5,MT
    (7) ~D . ~I   6,5,Conj.
    (8) W   4,7,MP

5   (1) S ⊃ P
    (2) C ⊃ ~F
    (3) I ⊃ F
    (4) O ⊃ ~P
    (5) O ∨ C   /∴ ~S ∨ ~I
    (6) (O ⊃ ~P) . (C ⊃ ~F)   4,2,Conj.
    (7) ~P ∨ ~F   6,5,CD
    (8) (S ⊃ P) . (I ⊃ F)   1,3,Conj.
    (9) ~S ∨ ~I   8,7,DD

6   (1) (~K . P) ⊃ (B ∨ R)
    (2) ~K ⊃ (B ⊃ D)
    (3) K ∨ (R ⊃ E)

	(4)	~K . P	/∴ D ∨ E
	(5)	B ∨ R	1,4,MP
	(6)	~K	4,Simp.
	(7)	B ⊃ D	2,6,MP
	(8)	R ⊃ E	3,6,DS
	(9)	(B ⊃ D) . (R ⊃ E)	7,8,Conj.
	(10)	D ∨ E	9,5,CD
7	(1)	C ⊃ N	
	(2)	N ⊃ I	
	(3)	I ⊃ S	
	(4)	(C ⊃ S) ⊃ (N ⊃ C)	
	(5)	~C	/∴ ~N
	(6)	C ⊃ I	1,2,HS
	(7)	C ⊃ S	6,3,HS
	(8)	N ⊃ C	4,7,MP
	(9)	~N	8,5,MT
8	(1)	(A ⊃ B) . (B ⊃ ~C)	
	(2)	C ⊃ ~D	
	(3)	B ⊃ E	
	(4)	~D ⊃ F	
	(5)	~E ∨ ~F	/∴ ~A ∨ ~C
	(6)	A ⊃ B	1,Simp.
	(7)	A ⊃ E	6,3,HS
	(8)	C ⊃ F	2,4,HS
	(9)	(A ⊃ E) . (C ⊃ F)	7,8,Conj.
	(10)	~A ∨ ~C	9,5,DD
9	(1)	(G ∨ H) ⊃ ~I	
	(2)	I ∨ H	
	(3)	(H ∨ ~G) ⊃ J	
	(4)	G	/∴ J ∨ ~H
	(5)	G ∨ H	4,Add.
	(6)	~I	1,5,MP
	(7)	H	2,6,DS
	(8)	H ∨ ~G	7,Add.
	(9)	J	3,8,MP
	(10)	J ∨ ~H	9,Add.
10	(1)	(R ⊃ P) . (~P ⊃ H)	
	(2)	(M ⊃ D) . (D ⊃ R)	
	(3)	(~M ∨ ~R) ⊃ (~P ∨ ~D)	
	(4)	~M	/∴ ~R ∨ ~M
	(5)	~M ∨ ~R	4,Add.
	(6)	~P ∨ ~D	3,5,MP

	(7) R ⊃ P	1,Simp.
	(8) M ⊃ D	2,Simp.
	(9) (R ⊃ P) . (M ⊃ D)	7,8,Conj.
	(10) ~R ∨ ~M	9,6,DD
11	(1) A ⊃ B	
	(2) C ⊃ D	
	(3) ~B ∨ ~D	
	(4) ~E	
	(5) (~A ∨ ~C) ⊃ (E ∨ F)	/∴ F
	(6) (A ⊃ B) . (C ⊃ D)	1,2,Conj.
	(7) ~A ∨ ~C	6,3,DD
	(8) E ∨ F	5,7,MP
	(9) F	8,4,DS
12	(1) (A . B) ⊃ [(A ⊃ (D . E)]	
	(2) (A . B) . C	/∴ D ∨ E
	(3) A . B	2,Simp.
	(4) A ⊃ (D . E)	1,3,MP
	(5) A	3,Simp.
	(6) D . E	4,5,MP
	(7) D	6,Simp.
	(8) D ∨ E	7,Add.

Section 6 page 119

1	(1) ~E ∨ F	
	(2) E	/∴ F
	(3) ~~E	2,DN
	(4) F	1,3,DS
2	(1) ~C ∨ ~D	/∴ ~(C . D)
	(2) ~(C . D)	1,de M.
3	(1) ~(C ∨ D)	/∴ ~C . ~D
	(2) ~C . ~D	1,de M.
4	(1) R ∨ (U . W)	/∴ R ∨ W
	(2) R ∨ (W . U)	1,Comm.
	(3) (R ∨ W) . (R ∨ U)	2,Dist.
	(4) R ∨ W	3,Simp.
5	(1) (A ∨ B) . (A ∨ C)	
	(2) ~A	/∴ B.C
	(3) A ∨ (B . C)	1,Dist.
	(4) B . C	3,2,DS
6	(1) A ∨ (B ∨ C)	/∴ (A ∨ B) ∨ C
	(2) (A ∨ B) ∨ C	1,Assn.

7 (1) A ∨ (B ∨ C)   /∴ C ∨ (A ∨ B)
 (2) (A ∨ B) ∨ C   1,Assn.
 (3) C ∨ (A ∨ B)   2,Comm.
8 (1) A ∨ (B ∨ C)
 (2) ∼C   /∴ A ∨ B
 (3) (A ∨ B) v C   1,Assn.
 (4) C ∨ (A v B)   3,Comm.
 (5) A ∨ B   4,2,DS
9 (1) (X ∨ N) ⊃ (Y . P)
 (2) N ∨ X   /∴ Y . P
 (3) X ∨ N   2,Comm.
 (4) Y . P   1,3,MP
10 (1) (X ∨ N) ⊃ (Y . P)
 (2) N ∨ X   /∴ Y
 (3) X ∨ N   2,Comm.
 (4) Y . P   1,3,MP
 (5) Y   4,Simp.
11 (1) (X ∨ N) ⊃ (Y . P)
 (2) N ∨ X   /∴ P
 (3) X ∨ N   2,Comm.
 (4) Y . P   1,3,MP
 (5) P . Y   4,Comm.
 (6) P   5,Simp.
12 (1) N ∨ (M ∨ V)
 (2) ∼(M ∨ V)   /∴ N
 (3) (M ∨ V) ∨ N   1,Comm.
 (4) N   3,2,DS
13 (1) [(F ∨ G) . (H ⊃ I)] . (J . K)
         /∴ J . K
 (2) (J . K) . [(F ∨ G) . (H ⊃ I)]
         1,Comm.
 (3) J . K   2,Simp.
14 (1) [(F ∨ G) . (H ⊃ I)] . (J . K)
         /∴ K
 (2) (J . K) . [(F ∨ G) . (H ⊃ I)]
         1,Comm.
 (3) J . K   2,Simp.
 (4) K . J   3,Comm.
 (5) K   4,Simp.
15 (1) [(F ∨ G) . (H ⊃ I)] . (J . K)
         /∴ J ∨ N

	(2) (J . K) . [(F ∨ G) . (H ⊃ I)]	
		1,Comm.
	(3) J . K	2,Simp.
	(4) J	3,Simp.
	(5) J ∨ N	4,Add.
16	(1) K . (L ∨ W)	
	(2) ~(K . L)	/∴ K . W
	(3) (K . L) ∨ (K . W)	1,Dist.
	(4) K . W	3,2,DS
17	(1) (P . Q) ∨ (P . R)	/∴ P
	(2) P . (Q ∨ R)	1,Dist.
	(3) P	2,Simp.
18	(1) (Z ∨ Y) . (Z ∨ K)	
	(2) ~(Y . K)	/∴ Z
	(3) Z ∨ (Y . K)	1,Dist.
	(4) (Y . K) ∨ Z	3,Comm.
	(5) Z	4,2,DS
19	(1) ~(~E ∨ ~G)	/∴ E
	(2) ~~E . ~~G	1,de M.
	(3) E . G	2,DN
	(4) E	3,Simp.
20	(1) ~(~H ∨ ~I)	/∴ I
	(2) ~~H . ~~I	1,de M.
	(3) ~~I . ~~H	2,Comm.
	(4) ~~I	3,Simp.
	(5) I	4,DN
21	(1) H ⊃ (K . L)	
	(2) ~K	/∴ ~H
	(3) ~K ∨ ~L	2,Add.
	(4) ~(K . L)	3,de M.
	(5) ~H	1,4,MT
22	(1) ~(V ∨ W) . R	/∴ R
	(2) R . ~(V ∨ W)	1,Comm.
	(3) R	2,Simp.
23	(1) ~(V ∨ W) . R	/∴ ~V
	(2) (~V . ~W) . R	1,de M.
	(3) ~V . (~W . ~R)	2,Assn.
	(4) ~V	3,Simp.
24	(1) (P ⊃ Q) . (R ⊃ T)	
	(2) ~T	/∴ ~R
	(3) (R ⊃ T) . (P ⊃ Q)	1,Comm.

	(4) R ⊃ T	3,Simp.
	(5) ∼R	4, 2, MT
25	(1) (P ∨ Q) ∨ [(R ∨ S) . (T ∨ U)]	
	(2) ∼P	
	(3) ∼Q	/∴ R ∨ S
	(4) ∼P . ∼Q	2,3,Conj.
	(5) ∼(P ∨ Q)	4,de M.
	(6) (R ∨ S) . (T ∨ U)	1,5,DS
	(7) R ∨ S	6,Simp.

Section 6 contd. *page 123*

(A) 1	(1) ∼A ∨ B	/∴ A ⊃ B
	(2) A ⊃ B	1,Mat.Imp.
2	(1) ∼H ⊃ ∼I	
	(2) I	/∴ H
	(3) I ⊃ H	1,Trans.
	(4) H	3,2,MP
3	(1) S ≡ P	/∴ (S ⊃ P) . (P ⊃ S)
	(2) (S ⊃ P) . (P ⊃ S)	1,Mat.Equiv.
4	(1) S ≡ P	/∴ P ⊃ S
	(2) (S ⊃ P) . (P ⊃ S)	1,Mat.Equiv.
	(3) (P ⊃ S) . (S ⊃ P)	2,Comm.
	(4) P ⊃ S	3,Simp.
5	(1) P . Q	/∴ P ≡ Q
	(2) (P . Q) ∨ (∼P . ∼Q)	1,Add.
	(3) P ≡ Q	2,Mat.Equiv.
6	(1) R ⊃ J	/∴ ∼J ⊃ ∼R
	(2) ∼J ⊃ ∼R	1,Trans.
7	(1) ∼L ⊃ ∼M	/∴ ∼M ∨ L
	(2) M ⊃ L	1,Trans.
	(3) ∼M ∨ L	2,Mat.Imp.
8	(1) (P ⊃ Q) . (R ⊃ Q)	
	(2) P ∨ R	/∴ Q
	(3) Q ∨ Q	1,2,CD
	(4) Q	3,Taut.
9	(1) (C . D) ⊃ J	/∴ C ⊃ (D ⊃ J)
	(2) C ⊃ (D ⊃ J)	1,Exp.
10	(1) (F . G) ⊃ J	
	(2) (G ⊃ J) ⊃ C	/∴ F ⊃ C
	(3) F ⊃ (G ⊃ J)	1,Exp.
	(4) F ⊃ C	3,2,HS

(B) 1   (1) (S . U) ⊃ P
      (2) (U ⊃ P) ⊃ W
      (3) S   /∴ W
      (4) S ⊃ (U ⊃ P)   1,Exp.
      (5) U ⊃ P   4,3,MP
      (6) W   2,5, MP

   2   (1) A ∨ (B . C)
      (2) (A ∨ B) ⊃ D   /∴ C ∨ D
      (3) (A ∨ B) . (A ∨ C) 1,Dist.
      (4) A ∨ B   3,Simp.
      (5) D   2,4,MP
      (6) D ∨ C   5,Add.
      (7) C ∨ D   6,Comm.

   3   (1) G ⊃ (B ⊃ C)
      (2) G . ~C   /∴ ~B
      (3) G   2,Simp.
      (4) B ⊃ C   1,3,MP
      (5) ~C . G   2,Comm.
      (6) ~C   5,Simp.
      (7) ~B   4,6,MT

   4   (1) P ⊃ S   /∴ P ⊃ (H ⊃ S)
      (2) ~P ∨ S   1,Mat.Imp.
      (3) (~P ∨ S) ∨ ~H 2,Add.
      (4) ~P ∨ (S ∨ ~H) 3,Assn.
      (5) ~P ∨ (~H ∨ S) 4,Comm.
      (6) P ⊃ (~H ∨ S)   5,Mat.Imp.
      (7) P ⊃ (H ⊃ S)   6,Mat.Imp.

   5   (1) (F ⊃ R) . (L ⊃ U)
      (2) (R . U) ⊃ C
      (3) ~C   /∴ ~F ∨ ~L
      (4) ~(R . U)   2,3,MT
      (5) ~R ∨ ~U   4,de M.
      (6) ~F ∨ ~L   1,5,DD

   6   (1) (~A ∨ B) . (A ⊃ C)
      (2) B ⊃ (C ⊃ E)   /∴ A ⊃ E
      (3) (~A ∨ B) . (~A ∨ C) 1,Mat.Imp.
      (4) ~A ∨ (B . C)   3,Dist.
      (5) A ⊃ (B . C)   4,Mat.Imp.
      (6) (B . C) ⊃ E   2,Exp.
      (7) A ⊃ E   5,6,H.S.

   7   (1) B
      (2) (C . B) ⊃ ~M

	(3)	M	/∴ ~C
	(4)	~~M	3,DN
	(5)	~(C . B)	2,4,MT
	(6)	~C ∨ ~B	5,de M.
	(7)	~B ∨ ~C	6,Comm.
	(8)	~~B	1,DN
	(9)	~C	7,8,DS
8	(1)	(A ⊃ B) . (C ⊃ B)	
	(2)	D ⊃ (A ∨ C)	
	(3)	D	/∴ B
	(4)	A ∨ C	2,3,MP
	(5)	B ∨ B	1,4,CD
	(6)	B	5,Taut.
9	(1)	~K ∨ L	
	(2)	~M ⊃ ~L	/∴ K ⊃ M
	(3)	K ⊃ L	1,Mat.Imp.
	(4)	L ⊃ M	2,Trans.
	(5)	K ⊃ M	3,4,HS
10	(1)	(A . B) ⊃ (C v D)	
	(2)	D ⊃ E	
	(3)	E ⊃ F	
	(4)	~(F . G)	
	(5)	G . ~C	/∴ A ⊃ ~B
	(6)	~F ∨ ~G	4,de M.
	(7)	~G ∨ ~F	6,Comm.
	(8)	G ⊃ ~F	7,Mat.Imp.
	(9)	G	5,Simp.
	(10)	~F	8,9,MP
	(11)	~E	3,10,MT
	(12)	~D	2,11,MT
	(13)	~C . G	5,Comm.
	(14)	~C	13,Simp.
	(15)	~C . ~D	14,12,Conj.
	(16)	~(C ∨ D)	15,deM.
	(17)	~(A . B)	1,16,MT
	(18)	~A ∨ ~B	17,de M.
	(19)	A ⊃ ~B	18,Mat.Imp.
11	(1)	G ⊃ (S ⊃ U)	
	(2)	G . ~U	/∴ ~S
	(3)	G	2,Simp.
	(4)	S ⊃ U	1,3,MP
	(5)	~U . G	2,Comm.

	(6)	~U	5,Simp.
	(7)	~S	4,6,MT
12	(1)	(C ⊃ E) . (P ⊃ L)	
	(2)	(L . E) ⊃ S	
	(3)	~S	/∴ ~C ∨ ~P
	(4)	~(L . E)	2,3,MT
	(5)	~L ∨ ~E	4,de M.
	(6)	~E ∨ ~L	5,Comm.
	(7)	~C ∨ ~P	1,6,DD
13	(1)	[(A . B) ⊃ C] . [(A . ~B) ⊃ ~C]	
			/∴ A ⊃ (B ≡ C)
	(2)	[A ⊃ (B ⊃ C)] . [A ⊃ (~B ⊃ ~C)]	
			1, Exp.
	(3)	[~A ∨ (B ⊃ C)] . [~A ∨ (~B ⊃ ~C)]	
			2, Mat.Imp.
	(4)	~A ∨ [(B ⊃ C) . (~B ⊃ ~C)]	
			3, Dist.
	(5)	A ⊃ [(B ⊃ C) . (~B ⊃ ~C)]	
			4,Mat.Imp.
	(6)	A ⊃ [(B ⊃ C) . (C ⊃ B)]	
			5,Trans.
	(7)	A ⊃ (B ≡ C)	6,Mat.Equiv.
14	(1)	(J . S) ⊃ W	
	(2)	W ⊃ T	
	(3)	~T . J	/∴ ~S
	(4)	(J . S) ⊃ T	1,2,HS
	(5)	~T	3,Simp.
	(6)	~(J . S)	4,5,MT
	(7)	~J ∨ ~S	6,de M.
	(8)	J ⊃ ~S	7,Mat.Imp.
	(9)	J . ~T	3,Comm.
	(10)	J	9,Simp.
	(11)	~S	8,10,MP
15	(1)	H ⊃ ~E	
	(2)	~S . E	
	(3)	E ⊃ (D ∨ S)	/∴ D ∨ H
	(4)	E . ~S	2,Comm.
	(5)	E	4,Simp.
	(6)	D ∨ S	3,5,MP
	(7)	S ∨ D	6,Comm.
	(8)	~S	2,Simp.
	(9)	D	7,8, DS
	(10)	D ∨ H	9,Add.

16 (1) A ⊃ (F . ~G)
    (2) (~G ∨ R) ⊃ ~P
    (3) P . ~Q   /∴ ~A
    (4) P   3,Simp.
    (5) ~~P   4,DN
    (6) ~(~G ∨ R)   2,5,MT
    (7) ~~G . ~R   6,de M.
    (8) ~~G   7,Simp.
    (9) ~~G ∨ ~F   8,Add.
    (10) ~F ∨ ~~G   9,Comm.
    (11) ~(F . ~G)   10,de M.
    (12) ~A   1,11,MT

17 (1) (P ∨ Q) . (P ∨ R)
    (2) P ⊃ S
    (3) S ⊃ T
    (4) (Q . R) ⊃ (U ⊃ T)
    (5) ~T   /∴ ~U
    (6) P ∨ (Q . R)   1,Dist.
    (7) ~P ⊃ (Q . R)   6,Mat.Imp.
    (8) P ⊃ T   2,3,HS
    (9) ~P   8,5,MT
    (10) Q . R   7,9,MP
    (11) U ⊃ T   4,10,MP
    (12) ~U   11,5,MT

18 (1) B ∨ T
    (2) (B ∨ C) ⊃ (L . M)
    (3) ~L   /∴ T
    (4) ~L ∨ ~M   3,Add.
    (5) ~(L . M)   4,de M.
    (6) ~(B ∨ C)   2,5,MT
    (7) ~B . ~C   6,de M.
    (8) ~B   7,Simp.
    (9) T   1,8,DS

19 (1) (P . Q) ∨ (R . S)
    (2) P ⊃ ~P   /∴ S
    (3) ~P ∨ ~P   2,Mat.Imp.
    (4) ~P   3,Taut.
    (5) ~P ∨ ~Q   4,Add.
    (6) ~(P . Q)   5,de M.
    (7) R . S   1,6,DS
    (8) S . R   7,Comm.
    (9) S   8,Simp.

20   (1) $(P \lor S) \supset (I \cdot C)$
     (2) $I \supset N$
     (3) $\sim N$ $/\therefore \sim P$
     (4) $\sim I$ 2,3,MT
     (5) $\sim I \lor \sim C$ 4,Add.
     (6) $\sim(I \cdot C)$ 5,de M.
     (7) $\sim(P \lor S)$ 1,6,MT
     (8) $\sim P \cdot \sim S$ 7,de M.
     (9) $\sim P$ 8,Simp.

21   (1) $(J \lor S) \supset (C \cdot V)$ $/\therefore \sim J \lor C$
     (2) $\sim(J \lor S) \lor (C \cdot V)$ 1,Mat.Imp.
     (3) $(\sim J \cdot \sim S) \lor (C \cdot V)$ 2,de M.
     (4) $[(\sim J \cdot \sim S) \lor C] \cdot [(\sim J \cdot \sim S) \lor V]$
                                   3,Dist.
     (5) $(\sim J \cdot \sim S) \lor C$ 4,Simp.
     (6) $C \lor (\sim J \cdot \sim S)$ 5,Comm.
     (7) $(C \lor \sim J) \cdot (C \lor \sim S)$ 6,Dist.
     (8) $C \lor \sim J$ 7,Simp.
     (9) $\sim J \lor C$ 8,Comm.

22   (1) $(R \supset W) \cdot (P \supset M)$
     (2) $R \lor P$
     (3) $(R \supset \sim M) \cdot (P \supset \sim W)$ $/\therefore M \equiv \sim W$
     (4) $W \lor M$ 1,2,CD
     (5) $\sim M \lor \sim W$ 3,2,CD
     (6) $\sim\sim W \lor M$ 4,DN
     (7) $\sim W \supset M$ 6,Mat.Imp.
     (8) $M \supset \sim W$ 5,Mat.Imp.
     (9) $(M \supset \sim W) \cdot (\sim W \supset M)$ 8,7,Conj.
    (10) $M \equiv \sim W$ 9,Mat.Equiv.

23   (1) $D \lor (R \cdot F)$
     (2) $D \supset F$ $/\therefore F$
     (3) $(D \lor R) \cdot (D \lor F)$ 1,Dist.
     (4) $(D \lor F) \cdot (D \lor R)$ 3,Comm.
     (5) $D \lor F$ 4,Simp.
     (6) $F \lor D$ 5,Comm.
     (7) $\sim\sim F \lor D$ 6,DN
     (8) $\sim F \supset D$ 7,Mat.Imp.
     (9) $\sim F \supset F$ 8,2, HS
    (10) $\sim\sim F \lor F$ 9,Mat.Imp.
    (11) $F \lor F$ 10,DN
    (12) F 11,Taut.

24   (1) W ⊃ M
     (2) M ⊃ ~(L . G)
     (3) (~L ⊃ D) . ~D
     (4) G   /∴ ~W
     (5) W ⊃ ~(L . G)   1,2,HS
     (6) ~L ⊃ D   3,Simp.
     (7) ~D . (~L ⊃ D)   3,Comm.
     (8) ~D   7,Simp.
     (9) ~~L   6,8,MT
   (10) L   9,DN
   (11) L . G   10,4,Conj.
   (12) ~~(L . G)   11,DN
   (13) ~W   5,12,MT

25   (1) (S ⊃ A) . (A ⊃ ~R)
     (2) V ⊃ B
     (3) B ⊃ ~R
     (4) R ∨ F
     (5) S ∨ V   /∴ F
     (6) S ⊃ ~R   1,HS
     (7) V ⊃ ~R   2,3,HS
     (8) (S ⊃ ~R) . (V ⊃ ~R)   6,7,Conj.
     (9) ~R ∨ ~R   8,5,CD
   (10) ~R   9,Taut.
   (11) F   4,10,DS

Section 7   *page 127*

1   (1) A ⊃ (B . C)
     (2) (B ∨ C) ⊃ I   /∴ A ⊃ I
     (3) ~A ∨ (B . C)   1,Impl.
     (4) (~A ∨ B) . (~A ∨ C)   3,Dist.
     (5) (~A ∨ B)   4,Simp.
     (6) ~A ∨ (B ∨ C)   5,Add.Assoc.
     (7) A ⊃ (B ∨ C)   6,Impl.
     (8) A ⊃ I   2,7,HS

By conditional proof
     (3) A   /∴ I (C . P)
     (4) B . C   1,3,MP
     (5) B   4,Simp.
     (6) B ∨ C   5,Add.
     (7) I   2,6,MP
     (8) A ⊃ I   3–7,CP

2   (1) A ⊃ (B ∨ C)
     (2) B ⊃ C   /∴ A ⊃ C
     (3) A   /∴ C   (C . P)
     (4) B ∨ C   1,3,MP
     (5) ∼C ⊃ B   3,Comm.Impl.
     (6) ∼C ⊃ C   2,5,HS
     (7) C ∨ C   6,Impl.DN
     (8) C   7,Taut.
     (9) A ⊃ C   3–8,CP

3   (1) P ⊃ Q   /∴ P ⊃ ∼(P ⊃ ∼Q)
     (2) P   /∴ ∼(P ⊃ ∼Q)   (C . P)
     (3) Q   1,2,MP
     (4) P . Q   2,3,Conj.
     (5) ∼(∼P ∨ ∼Q)   4,de M, DN.
     (6) ∼(P ⊃ ∼Q)   5,Impl.
     (7) P ⊃ ∼(P ⊃ ∼Q)   2–6,CP

4   (1) D ⊃ (F ∨ T)
     (2) ∼F   /∴ ∼T ⊃ (∼D ∨ S)
     (3) ∼(F ∨ T) ⊃ ∼D   1,Trans.
     (4) (∼F . ∼T) ⊃ ∼D   3,de M.
     (5) ∼F ⊃ (∼T ⊃ ∼D)   4,Exp.
     (6) ∼T ⊃ ∼D   2,5,MP
     (7) T ∨ ∼D   6,Impl.DN
     (8) T ∨ (∼D ∨ S)   7,Add.Assoc.
     (9) ∼T ⊃ (∼D ∨ S)   8,Impl.

By conditional proof

     (3) ∼T   /∴ ∼D ∨ S   (CP)
     (4) ∼F . ∼T   2,3,Conj.
     (5) ∼(F ∨ T)   4,de M
     (6) ∼D   1,5,MT
     (7) ∼D ∨ S   6,Add.
     (8) ∼T ⊃ (∼D ∨ S)   3–7,CP

5   (1) (E . S) ⊃ P
     (2) (E . ∼S) ⊃ ∼P   /∴ E ⊃ [(S . P) ∨ (∼S . ∼P)]
     (3) E   /∴ (S . P) ∨ (∼S . ∼P)   (CP)
     (4) E ⊃ (S ⊃ P)   1,Exp.
     (5) E ⊃ (∼S ⊃ ∼P)   2,Exp.
     (6) S ⊃ P   3,4,MP
     (7) ∼S ⊃ ∼P   3,5,MP
     (8) P ⊃ S   7,Trans.
     (9) (S ⊃ P) . (P ⊃ S)   6,8,Conj.

    (10) S ≡ P   9,Equiv.
    (11) (S . P) ∨ (~S ∨ ~P)   10,Equiv.
    (12) E ⊃ [(S . P) ∨ (~S . ~P)
                               3–11,CP

6   (1) A . B
    (2) (A ∨ B) ⊃ F
    (3) F ⊃ (C ⊃ D)
    (4) D ⊃ E   /∴ C ⊃ E
    (5) A   1,Simp.
    (6) A ∨ B   5,Add.
    (7) F   2,6,MP
    (8) C ⊃ D   3,7,MP
    (9) C ⊃ E   4,8,HS

By conditional proof
    (5) C   /∴ E (CP)
    (6) A   1,Simp.
    (7) A ∨ B   6,Add.
    (8) F   2,7,MP
    (9) C ⊃ D   3,8,MP
    (10) D   5,9,MP
    (11) E   4,10,MP
    (12) C ⊃ E   5–11, CP

Note that conditional proof gives us no advantage in brevity here.
But even if a conditional proof is not shorter than a direct proof
it may be easier.

7   (1) P ⊃ (Q ⊃ ~P)
    (2) P ⊃ Q
    (3) ~P ⊃ ~Q   /∴ P ⊃ (P . Q)
    (4) Q ⊃ P   3,Trans.
    (5) P ⊃ P   2,4,HS
    (6) (P ⊃ P) . (P ⊃ Q)   2,5,Conj.
    (7) (~P ∨ P) . (~P ∨ Q) 6,Impl.
    (8) ~P ∨ (P . Q)   7,Dist.
    (9) P ⊃ (P . Q)   8,Impl.

By conditional proof
    (4) P   /∴ P . Q (CP)
    (5) Q   2,4,MP
    (6) P . Q   4,5,Conj.
    (7) P ⊃ (P . Q)   4–6,CP
8   (1) (A ∨ B) ⊃ (C . D)   /∴ A ⊃ C

    (2) ~(A ∨ B) ∨ (C . D)   1,Impl.
    (3) (~A . ~B) ∨ (C . D)   2,de M.
    (4) [(~A . ~B) ∨ C] . [(~A . ~B) ∨ D]
                                    3,Dist.
    (5) (~A . ~B) ∨ C   4,Simp.
    (6) C ∨ (~A . ~B)   5,Comm.
    (7) (C ∨ ~A) . (C ∨ ~B)   6,Dist.
    (8) C ∨ ~A   7,Simp.
    (9) ~A ∨ C   8,Comm.
   (10) A ⊃ C   9,Impl.

By conditional proof
    (2) A   /∴ C (CP)
    (3) A ∨ B   2,Add.
    (4) C . D   1,3,MP
    (5) C   4,Simp.
    (6) A ⊃ C   2–5,CP
 9 (1) (A ∨ B) ⊃ (C . D)
    (2) B   /∴ ~D ⊃ A
    (3) B ∨ A   2,Add.
    (4) A ∨ B   3,Comm.
    (5) C . D   1,4,MP
    (6) D   5,Comm.Simp.
    (7) D ∨ A   6,Add.
    (8) ~D ⊃ A   7,Impl.

By conditional proof
    (3) ~D   /∴ A (CP)
    (4) ~(C . D) ⊃ ~(A ∨ B)   1,Trans.
    (5) (~C ∨ ~D) ⊃ (~A . ~B)
                                      4,de M.
    (6) ~C ∨ ~D   3,Add.Comm.
    (7) ~A . ~B   5,6,MP
    (8) ~B   7,Comm.Simp.
    (9) ~B ∨ A   8,Add.
   (10) A   8,9,DS
   (11) ~D ⊃ A   3–10,CP

Note that here again we are better off with a direct proof.

10 (1) (Q . R) ⊃ S
    (2) (R ⊃ S) ⊃ T   /∴ Q ⊃ T
    (3) Q ⊃ (R ⊃ S)   1,Exp.
    (4) Q ⊃ T   2,3,HS

By conditional proof

    (3) Q   /∴ T (CP)
    (4) Q ⊃ (R ⊃ S)   1,Exp.
    (5) R ⊃ S   3,4,MP
    (6) T   2,5,MP
    (7) Q ⊃ T   3–6,CP

Section 8   *page 129*

1   (1) (D ∨ E) ⊃ (F ⊃ G)
     (2) (∼G ∨ H) ⊃ (D . F)   /∴ G
     (3) ∼G   IP
     (4) ∼G ∨ H   3,Add.
     (5) D . F   2,4,MP
     (6) D   5,Simp.
     (7) D ∨ E   6,Add.
     (8) F ⊃ G   1,7,MP
     (9) F   5,Comm.Simp.
   (10) G   8,9,MP
   (11) G . ∼G   3,10,Conj.

2   (1) (H ⊃ I) . (J ⊃ K)
     (2) (I ∨ K) ⊃ L
     (3) ∼L   /∴ ∼(H ∨ J)
     (4) ∼∼(H ∨ J)   IP
     (5) H ∨ J   4,DN
     (6) I ∨ K   1,5,CD
     (7) L   2,6,MP
     (8) L . ∼L   3,7,Conj.

3   (1) (V ⊃ ∼W) . (X ⊃ Y)
     (2) (∼W ⊃ Z) . (Y ⊃ ∼A)
     (3) (Z ⊃ ∼B) . (∼A ⊃ C)
     (4) V . X   /∴ ∼B . C
     (5) ∼(∼B . C)   IP
     (6) ∼∼B ∨ ∼C   5, de M
     (7) ∼Z ∨ A   3,7,DD,DN
     (8) ∼Z ∨ ∼∼A   8,DN
     (9) W ∨ ∼Y   2,9,DD,DN
   (10) ∼V . ∼X   1,10,DD,DN
   (11) (V . X) . (∼V . ∼X)   4,11,Conj.

4   (1) P
     (2) (∼P ∨ ∼S) ⊃ (∼P . ∼R)
                           /∴ S
     (3) ∼S   IP

	(4)	∼P ∨ ∼S	3,Add.Comm.
	(5)	∼P . ∼R	2,4,MP
	(6)	∼P	5,Simp.
	(7)	P . ∼P	1,6,Conj.
5	(1)	A ⊃ (F . ∼G)	
	(2)	(∼G ∨ R) ⊃ ∼P	
	(3)	P . Q	/∴ ∼A
	(4)	∼∼A	IP
	(5)	A	4,DN
	(6)	(F . ∼G)	1,5,MP
	(7)	∼G	6,Comm.Simp.
	(8)	∼G ∨ R	7,Add.
	(9)	∼P	2,8,MP
	(10)	P	3,Simp.
	(11)	P . ∼P	9,10,Conj.
6	(1)	B ∨ T	
	(2)	(B ∨ C) ⊃ (L . M)	
	(3)	∼L	/∴ T
	(4)	∼T	IP
	(5)	T ∨ B	1,Comm.
	(6)	B	5,4,DS
	(7)	B ∨ C	5,Add.
	(8)	L.M	2,6,MP
	(9)	L	7,Simp.
	(10)	L . ∼L	3,8,Conj.
7	(1)	A ⊃ (F . ∼G)	
	(2)	(∼G ∨ R) ⊃ ∼P	
	(3)	P . ∼Q	/∴ ∼A
	(4)	∼∼A	IP
	(5)	A	4,DN
	(6)	F . ∼G	1,5,MP
	(7)	∼G	6,Comm.Simp.
	(8)	∼G ∨ R	7,Add.
	(9)	∼P	2,7,MP
	(10)	P	3,Simp.
	(11)	P . ∼P	9,10,Conj.
8	(1)	A ⊃ B	
	(2)	∼A ⊃ C	/∴ B ∨ C
	(3)	∼(B ∨ C)	IP
	(4)	∼B . ∼C	3,de M.
	(5)	∼B	4,Simp.

(6) ~A	1,5,MT
(7) ~C ⊃ A	2,Trans.DN
(8) ~C	4,Comm.Simp.
(9) A	7,8,MP
(10) A . ~A	8,9,Conj.

Note that a direct proof of 8 is shorter than an indirect proof.
Thus:

	(3) ~B ⊃ ~A	1, Trans.
	(4) ~B ⊃ C	2, 3, HS
	(5) B ∨ C	4, Impl.DN
9	(1) W ⊃ M	
	(2) M ⊃ ~E	
	(3) ~(E ⊃ F)	/∴ ~W
	(4) W	IP
	(5) M	1,4,MP
	(6) ~E	2,5,MP
	(7) ~(~E ∨ F)	3,Impl.
	(8) E . ~F	7,de M.,DN
	(9) E	8,Simp.
	(10) E . ~E	6,9,Conj.
10	(1) (A . B) ⊃ (C ∨ D)	
	(2) D ⊃ E	
	(3) E ⊃ F	
	(4) ~(F . G)	
	(5) G . ~C	/∴ A ⊃ ~B
	(6) ~(A ⊃ ~B)	IP
	(7) ~(~A ∨ ~ B)	6, Impl.
	(8) A . B	7, de M., DN
	(9) C ∨ D	1,7,MP
	(10) ~C	5,Comm.Simp.
	(11) D	8,9,DS
	(12) E	2,10,MP
	(13) F	3,11,MP
	(14) ~F ∨ ~G	4,de M.
	(15) F ⊃ ~G	13,Impl.
	(16) ~G	12,14,MP
	(17) G	5,Simp.
	(18) G . ~G	15,16,Conj.

Exercises on Part II   *page 130*

(A) 1 (1) G ∨ F
        (2) ~B ⊃ ~F
        (3) B ⊃ R
                                       /∴ ~R ⊃ G
        (4) ~F ⊃ G   1,Comm.Impl.
        (5) ~R ⊃ ~B   3,Trans.
        (6) ~R ⊃ ~F   2,5,HS
        (7) ~R ⊃ G   4,6,HS
     2 (1) (R . E) ⊃ (O . I)
        (2) E ⊃ ~I
                                       /∴ ~E ∨ ~R
        (3) ~(~E ∨ ~R)   Indirect Proof
        (4) E . R   3,de M.,DN
        (5) E   4,Simp.
        (6) ~I   2,5,MP
        (7) ~(O . I) ⊃ ~(R . E)   1,Trans.
        (8) (~O ∨ ~I) ⊃ ~(R . E)   7,de M.
        (9) ~O ∨ ~I   6,Add.Comm.
       (10) ~(R . E)   8,9,MP
       (11) ~(E . R)   10,Comm.
       (12) (E . R) . ~(E . R)   4,11,Conj.
     3 (1) (A . P) ⊃ S
        (2) S ⊃ (C . O)
        (3) ~O
                                       /∴ A ⊃ ~P
        (4) ~S ⊃ ~(A . P)   1,Trans.
        (5) ~(C . O) ⊃ ~S   2,Trans.
        (6) ~(C . O) ⊃ ~(A . P)   4,5,HS
        (7) ~C ∨ ~O   3,Add.Comm.
        (8) ~(C . O)   7,de M.
        (9) ~(A . P)   6,8,MP
       (10) ~A ∨ ~P   9,de M.
       (11) A ⊃ ~P   10,Impl.
     5 (1) ~(P . ~T) ⊃ I
        (2) I ⊃ F
        (3) ~F
                                       /∴ ~(~P ∨ T)
        (4) ~I   2,3,MT
        (5) P . ~T   1,4,MT,DN
        (6) ~(~P ∨ T)   5,de M.,DN

6   (1) A ⊃ B
     (2) B ⊃ C
                           /∴ ~C ⊃ ~A
     (3) A ⊃ C   1,2,HS
     (4) ~C ⊃ ~A   3,Trans.

7   (1) G ⊃ P
     (2) I ⊃ ~P
     (3) I
                           /∴ ~G
     (4) ~P   2,3,MP
     (5) ~G   1,4,MT

8   (1) A ⊃ [C ⊃ (D . W)]
     (2) C . ~D
                           /∴ ~A
     (3) A   IP
     (4) C ⊃ (D . W)   1,3,MP
     (5) C   2,Simp.
     (6) D . W   4,5,MP
     (7) D   6,Simp.
     (8) ~D   2,Comm.Simp.
     (9) D . ~D   7,8,Conj.
    (10) D   9,Simp.
    (11) ~D   2,Comm.Simp.
    (12) D . ~D   10,11,Contradiction

9   (1) ~F ⊃ V
     (2) ~(F ∨ ~S)
     (3) ~P ⊃ ~S
                           /∴ V . P
     (4) ~F . S   2,de M.,DN.
     (5) ~F   4,Simp.
     (6) V   1,5,MP
     (7) S   4,Comm.Simp.
     (8) S ⊃ P   3,Trans.
     (9) P   7,8,MP
    (10) V . P   6,9,Conj.

10 (1) (P . L) ⊃ R
     (2) R ⊃ D
     (3) ~D
                          /∴ P ⊃ ~L
     (4) ~R   2,3,MT
     (5) ~(P . L)   1,4,MT

   (6) ~P ∨ ~L   5,de M.
   (7) P ⊃ ~L   6,Impl.
13 (1) J ⊃ S
   (2) B ⊃ ~S
                        /∴ J ⊃ ~B
   (3) S ⊃ ~B   2,Trans.,DN
   (4) J ⊃ ~B   1,3,HS
14 (1) (G ∨ B) ⊃ (J ∨ S)
   (2) (B ∨ J) ⊃ P
   (3) ~P . G
                        /∴ S
   (4) ~P   3,Simp.
   (5) ~(B ∨ J)   2,4,MT
   (6) ~B . ~J   5,de M.
   (7) G   3,Comm.Simp.
   (8) G ∨ B   7,Add.
   (9) J ∨ S   1,8,MP
  (10) ~J   6,Comm.Simp.
  (11) S   9,10,DS.
17 (1) P ⊃ (R ⊃ S)
   (2) ~R ⊃ H
   (3) ~S . ~H
   (4) P
                        /∴ E
   (5) R ⊃ S   1,4,MP
   (6) ~S   3,Simp.
   (7) ~R   5,6,MT
   (8) H   2,7,MP
   (9) ~H   3,Comm.Simp.
  (10) H ∨ E   8,Add.
  (11) E   9,10,DS

Note. This conclusion follows because of a contradiction
implied by the premises.

18 (1) D ⊃ (S ⊃ M)
   (2) ~R ∨ D
   (3) S
                        /∴ R ⊃ M
   (4) R ⊃ D   2,Impl.
   (5) R ⊃ (S ⊃ M)   1,4,HS
   (6) (R . S) ⊃ M   5,Exp.

	(7)	$(S . R) \supset M$	6,Comm.
	(8)	$S \supset (R \supset M)$	7,Exp.
	(9)	$R \supset M$	3,8,MP
19	(1)	$(F \lor B) \supset \sim G$	
	(2)	$\sim C \supset F$	
	(3)	$C \supset G$	
	(4)	$\sim F$	
			$/\therefore \sim B$
	(5)	C	2,4,MT,DN
	(6)	G	3,5,MP
	(7)	$\sim\sim G$	6,DN
	(8)	$\sim(F \lor B)$	1,7,MT
	(9)	$\sim F . \sim B$	8,de M.
	(10)	$\sim B$	9,Comm.Simp.

(B)

1	(1)	$\sim H \lor R$	
	(2)	H	
			$/\therefore R$
	(3)	$\sim\sim H$	2,DN
	(4)	R	1,3,DS
2	(1)	$H \lor B$	
	(2)	$\sim B$	
			$/\therefore H$
	(3)	$B \lor H$	1,Comm.
	(4)	H	2,3,DS
3	(1)	$\sim(M \lor V)$	
			$/\therefore \sim M$
	(2)	$\sim M . \sim V$	1,de M.
	(3)	$\sim M$	2,Simp.
4	(1)	$S \supset L$	
			$/\therefore S \supset (L \lor W)$
	(2)	$\sim S \lor L$	1,Impl.
	(3)	$(\sim S \lor L) \lor W$	2,Add.
	(4)	$\sim S \lor (L \lor W)$	3,Assoc.
	(5)	$S \supset (L \lor W)$	4,Impl.
5	(1)	$M \supset C$	
	(2)	$C \supset F$	
	(3)	$\sim F$	
			$/\therefore \sim M$
	(4)	$\sim C$	2,3,MT
	(5)	$\sim M$	1,4,MT

6 (1) W ∨ D
   (2) W ⊃ F
   (3) ∼F

                          /∴ D
   (4) ∼W   2,3,MT
   (5) D   1,4,DS

7 (1) B ⊃ D
   (2) (B ⊃ D) ∨ ∼A

                          /∴ (A . B) ⊃ D
   (3) (∼B ∨ D) ∨ ∼A   2,Impl.
   (4) ∼A ∨ (∼B ∨ D)   3,Comm.
   (5) (∼A ∨ ∼B) ∨ D   4,Assoc.
   (6) ∼(∼A ∨ ∼B) ⊃ D

                          5,Impl.
   (7) (A . B) ⊃ D   6,de M.

8 (1) (D . P) ⊃ B
   (2) (P ⊃ B) ⊃ C
   (3) D

                          /∴ C
   (4) D ⊃ (P ⊃ B)   1,Exp.
   (5) P ⊃ B   3,4,MP
   (6) C   2,5,MP

9 (1) G ⊃ (S ⊃ U)
   (2) G . ∼U

                          /∴ ∼S
   (3) G   2,Simp.
   (4) S ⊃ U   1,3,MP
   (5) ∼U   2,Comm.Simp.
   (6) ∼S   4,5,MT

10 (1) (C ⊃ E) . (P ⊃ L)
   (2) (L . E) ⊃ S
   (3) ∼S

                          /∴ ∼C ∨ ∼P
   (4) ∼(L . E)   2,3,MT
   (5) ∼L ∨ ∼E   4,de M.
   (6) ∼ E ∨ ∼ L   5,Comm.
   (7) ∼C ∨ ∼P   1,5,DD

11 (1) P ⊃ (Q . R)
   (2) (Q . R) ⊃ S
   (3) ∼S

                          /∴ P ⊃ Q
   (4) ∼(Q . R)   2,3,MT

	(5) ~P	1,4,MT
	(6) ~P ∨ Q	5,Add.
	(7) P ⊃ Q	6,Impl.
12	(1) F ⊃ G	
	(2) G ⊃ ~K	
	(3) ~K ⊃ M	
	(4) F . L	
		/∴ M ∨ L
	(5) F	4,Simp.
	(6) G	1,5,MP
	(7) ~K	2,6,MP
	(8) M	3,7,MP
	(9) M ∨ L	8,Add.
13	(1) (P ⊃ Q) ⊃ R	
	(2) (S ⊃ T) ⊃ U	
	(3) P ⊃ Q	
		/∴ R ∨ U
	(4) R	1,3,MP
	(5) R ∨ U	4,Add.
14	(1) P ⊃ (S . R)	
	(2) Q ⊃ ~(S . R)	
	(3) Q	
		/∴ P ⊃ T
	(4) ~(S . R)	2,3,MP
	(5) ~P	1,4,MT
	(6) ~P ∨ T	5,Add.
	(7) P ⊃ T	6,Impl.
15	(1) D ⊃ (F ∨ T)	
	(2) ~F	
		/∴ (D . ~S) ⊃ T
	(3) D ⊃ (~F ⊃ T)	1,Impl.DN
	(4) (D . ~F) ⊃ T	3,Exp.
	(5) (~F . D) ⊃ T	4,Comm.
	(6) ~F ⊃ (D ⊃ T)	5,Exp.
	(7) D ⊃ T	2,6,MP
	(8) ~D ∨ T	7,Impl.
	(9) (~D ∨ T) ∨ S	8,Add.
	(10) ~D ∨ (S ∨ T)	9,Assoc.,Comm.
	(11) (~D ∨ S) ∨ T	10,Assoc.
	(12) ~(~D ∨ S) ⊃ T	11,Impl.
	(13) (D . ~S) ⊃ T	12,de M.
16	(1) A ∨ B	

(2) $(A \lor C) \supset (D . E)$
(3) $\sim D$

/∴ $B . \sim C$

(4)	$\sim D \lor \sim E$	3,Add.
(5)	$\sim (D . E)$	4,de M.
(6)	$\sim (A \lor C)$	2,5,MT
(7)	$\sim A . \sim C$	6,de M.
(8)	$\sim A$	7,Simp.
(9)	B	1,8,DS
(10)	$\sim C$	7,Comm.Simp.
(11)	$B . \sim C$	9,10,Conj.

17 (1) $(A \lor B) \supset (C . D)$
     (2) $\sim C$

/∴ $\sim B$

(3)	$\sim (C . D) \supset \sim (A \lor B)$	1,Trans.
(4)	$\sim C \lor \sim D$	2,Add.
(5)	$\sim (C . D)$	4,de M.
(6)	$\sim (A \lor B)$	3,5,MP
(7)	$\sim A . \sim B$	6,de M.
(8)	$\sim B$	7,Comm.Simp.

18 (1) $A \supset B$
     (2) $B \supset \sim (C . D)$
     (3) $(\sim C \supset E) . \sim E$
     (4) D

/∴ $\sim A$

(5)	C	3,MT,DN
(6)	$C . D$	4,7,Conj.
(7)	$\sim\sim (C . D)$	8,DN
(8)	$\sim B$	2,9,MT
(9)	$\sim A$	1,10,MT

19 (1) $(P . Q) \supset R$
     (2) $(P \supset R) \supset S$
     (3) $\sim Q \lor T$

/∴ $Q \supset (S . T)$

(4)	$(Q . P) \supset R$	1,Comm.
(5)	$Q \supset (P \supset R)$	4,Exp.
(6)	$Q \supset S$	2,5,HS
(7)	$\sim Q \lor S$	6,Impl.
(8)	$(\sim Q \lor S) . (\sim Q \lor T)$	3,7,Conj.
(9)	$\sim Q \lor (S . T)$	8,Dist.

	(10)	Q ⊃ (S . T)	9,Impl.
20	(1)	(D ⊃ ∼P) . (P ⊃ Q)	
	(2)	Q ⊃ D	
	(3)	∼R ⊃ P	
			/∴ R
	(4)	D ⊃ ∼P	1,Simp.
	(5)	Q ⊃ ∼P	2,4,HS
	(6)	P ⊃ Q	1,Comm.Simp.
	(7)	P ⊃ ∼P	5,6,HS
	(8)	∼P ∨ ∼P	7,Impl.
	(9)	∼P	8,Taut.
	(10)	R	3,10,MT,DN
21	(1)	S ⊃ (T ⊃ U)	
	(2)	U ⊃ ∼U	
	(3)	(V ⊃ S) . (W ⊃ T)	
			/∴ V ⊃ ∼W
	(4)	(S . T) ⊃ U	1,Exp.
	(5)	∼U ∨ ∼U	2, Impl.
	(6)	∼U	5,Taut.
	(7)	∼(S . T)	4,6,MT
	(8)	∼S ∨ ∼T	7,de M.
	(9)	S ⊃ ∼T	8,Impl.
	(10)	V ⊃ S	3,Simp.
	(11)	V ⊃ ∼T	9,10,HS
	(12)	W ⊃ T	3,Comm.Simp.
	(13)	∼T ⊃ ∼W.	12,Trans.
	(14)	V ⊃ ∼W	11,13,HS
22	(1)	X ⊃ (Y ⊃ Z)	
	(2)	X ⊃ (A ⊃ B)	
	(3)	X . (Y ∨ A)	
	(4)	∼Z	
			/∴ B
	(5)	X	3,Simp.
	(6)	Y ⊃ Z	1,5,MP
	(7)	A ⊃ B	2,5,MP
	(8)	Y ∨ A	3,Comm.Simp.
	(9)	(Y ⊃ Z) . (A ⊃ B)	6,7,Conj.
	(10)	Z ∨ B	6,7,8,CD
	(11)	B	4,9,DS
23	(1)	C ⊃ (D ⊃ ∼C)	
	(2)	C ≡ D	
			/∴ ∼C . ∼D

(3) $(C \supset D) . (D \supset C)$

    2,Equiv.

(4) $C \supset (C \supset \sim D)$ 1,Trans.DN

(5) $(C . C) \supset \sim D$ 4,Exp.

(6) $C \supset \sim D$ 5,Taut.

(7) $C \supset D$ 3,Simp.

(8) $D \supset \sim C$ 6,Trans.DN

(9) $C \supset \sim C$ 7,8,HS

(10) $\sim C \vee \sim C$ 9,Impl.

(11) $\sim C$ 10,Taut.

(12) $D \supset C$ 3,Comm.Simp.

(13) $\sim D$ 11,12,MT

(14) $\sim C . \sim D$ 11,13,Conj.

24   (1) $E . (F \vee G)$

    (2) $(E . G) \supset \sim (H \vee I)$

    (3) $(\sim H \vee \sim I) \supset \sim (E . F)$

                   /∴ $H \equiv I$

    (4) $(E . F) \vee (E . G)$ 1,Dist.

    (5) $(E . F) \supset \sim (\sim H \vee \sim I)$

                   3,Trans.DN

    (6) $(E . F) \supset (H . I)$ 5,de M.

    (7) $(E . G) \supset (\sim H . \sim I)$

                   2,de M.

    (8) $[(E . F) \supset (H . I)] .$
        $[(E . G) \supset (\sim H . \sim I)]$ 6,7,Conj.

    (9) $(H . I) \vee (\sim H . \sim I)$

                   4,8,CD

  (10) $H \equiv I$ 8,Equiv.

25   (1) $(A \supset S) . (B \supset F)$

    (2) $A \vee B$

    (3) $(S \supset B) . (F \supset W)$

    (4) $\sim (A \vee G)$

                   /∴ W

    (5) $\sim A . \sim G$ 4,de M.

    (6) $\sim A$ 5,Simp.

    (7) B 2,6,DS

    (8) $B \supset F$ 1,Comm.Simp.

    (9) F 7,8,MP

  (10) $F \supset W$ 3,Comm.Simp.

  (11) W 9,10,MP

26   (1) $P \supset (Q \vee R)$

    (2) S ⊃ ~Q
    (3) (T ∨ U) ⊃ ~R
    (4) ~(S ⊃ ~T)

		/∴ ~P
(5)	~(~S ∨ ~T)	4,Impl.
(6)	S . T	5,de M.,DN
(7)	S	6,Simp.
(8)	~Q	2,7,MP
(9)	T	6,Comm. Simp.
(10)	T ∨ U	9,Add.
(11)	~R	3,10,MP
(12)	~Q . ~R	8,11,Conj.
(13)	~(Q ∨ R)	12,de M.
(14)	~P	1,13,MT

27 (1) (A . B) ⊃ (C ⊃ D)
    (2) ~E ⊃ ~D
    (3) ~(F ∨ G)
    (4) E ⊃ F

		/∴ (B . C) ⊃ ~A
(5)	B . C	/∴ ~A (CP)
(6)	[(A . B) . C] ⊃ D	1,Exp.
(7)	[(B . C) . A] ⊃ D	6,Assoc.Comm.
(8)	(B . C) ⊃ (A ⊃ D)	
		7,Exp.
(9)	A ⊃ D	5,8,MP
(10)	~F . ~G	3,de M.
(11)	~F	10,Simp.
(12)	~E	4,11,MT
(13)	~D	2,12,MP
(14)	~A	9,13,MT
(15)	(B . C) ⊃ ~A	5–14,CP

28 (1) A ⊃ (~B ⊃ C)
    (2) C ⊃ (A ⊃ D)
    (3) B ⊃ F
    (4) ~(A ⊃ F)
    (5) ~B

		/∴ D
(6)	~(~A ∨ F)	4,Impl.
(7)	A . ~F	6,de M.,DN
(8)	A	7,Simp.
(9)	~B ⊃ C	1,8,MP
(10)	C	5,9,MP

	(11) A ⊃ D	2,10,MP
	(12) D	8,11,MP
29	(1) F ⊃ G	
	(2) H ⊃ J	
	(3) K ⊃ (H ∨ M)	
	(4) ∼(L ⊃ G)	
	(5) ∼J ∨ F	
	(6) ∼M	
		/∴ ∼K
	(7) ∼(∼L ∨ G)	4,Impl.
	(8) L . ∼G	7,de M.,DN
	(9) ∼G	8,Comm.Simp.
	(10) ∼F	1,9,MT
	(11) F ∨ ∼J	5,Comm.
	(12) ∼J	10,11,DS
	(13) ∼H	2,12,MT
	(14) ∼H . ∼M	6,13,Conj.
	(15) ∼(H ∨ M)	14,de M.
	(16) ∼K	3,15,MT
30	(1) F ⊃ B	
	(2) ∼(H ⊃ ∼G)	
	(3) G ⊃ F	
	(4) (∼A ⊃ B) ⊃ (C . D)	
	(5) ∼J ⊃ ∼B	
		/∴ ∼A ⊃ J
	(6) ∼(∼H ∨ ∼G)	2,Impl.
	(7) H . G	6,de M.,DN
	(8) G	7,Comm.Simp.
	(9) F	3,8,MP
	(10) B	1,9,MP
	(11) J	10,DN, 5,MT,DN
	(12) J ∨ A	11,Add.
	(13) A ∨ J	12,Comm.
	(14) ∼A ⊃ J	13,Impl.
31	(1) P ⊃ Q	
		/∴ (P ⊃ ∼Q) ⊃ ∼P
	(2) P ⊃ ∼Q	/∴ ∼P (CP)
	(3) Q ⊃ ∼P	2,Trans. DN
	(4) P ⊃ ∼P	2,4,HS
	(5) ∼P ∨ ∼P	4,Impl.
	(6) ∼P	5,Taut.
	(7) (P ⊃ ∼Q) ⊃ ∼P	2–6,CP

32   (1) (P ∨ ∼Q) ⊃ R
      (2) S ⊃ (T ⊃ ∼R)
      (3) ∼(S ⊃ ∼T)

	/∴ P ⊃ T
(4) ∼(P ⊃ T)	Indirect Proof
(5) ∼(∼P ∨ T)	4,Impl.
(6) P . ∼T	5,de M.,DN
(7) ∼T	6,Comm.Simp.
(8) ∼(∼S ∨ ∼T)	3,Impl.
(9) S . T	8,de M, DN
(10) T	9,Comm.Simp.
(11) T . ∼T	7,10,Conj.

33   (1) A ⊃ (B . C)
      (2) C ⊃ (∼D ∨ ∼E)
      (3) ∼D ⊃ (E ⊃ F)
      (4) ∼E ⊃ ∼B

	/∴ A ⊃ F
(5) A	/∴ F (CP)
(6) B . C	1,5,MP
(7) B	6,Simp.
(8) E	4,8,DN,MT,DN
(9) C	6,Comm.Simp.
(10) ∼D ∨ ∼E	2,9,MP
(11) ∼E ∨ ∼D	10,Comm.
(12) ∼D	8,DN,11,DS
(13) E ⊃ F	3,12,MP
(14) F	8,13,MP
(15) A ⊃ F	5–14,CP

34   (1) (P ⊃ Q) ⊃ R

	/∴ P ⊃ (Q ⊃ R)
(2) ∼P ∨ Q) ⊃ R	1,Impl.
(3) ∼(∼P ∨ Q) ∨ R	2,Impl.
(4) (P .∼Q) ∨ R	3,de M.,DN
(5) R ∨ (P .∼Q)	4,Comm.
(6) (R ∨ P) . (R ∨ ∼Q)	5,Dist.
(7) R ∨ ∼Q	6,Comm.Simp.
(8) ∼Q ∨ R	7,Comm.
(9) Q ⊃ R	8,Impl.
(10) (Q ⊃ R) ∨ ∼P	9,Add.
(11) ∼P ∨ (Q ⊃ R)	10,Comm.
(12) P ⊃ (Q ⊃ R)	11,Impl.

35   (1) P ∨ Q   /∴ ~Q ⊃ [~R ⊃
                                               (~P ⊃ S)]

      (2) (P ∨ Q) ∨ (R ∨ S)   1,Add.
      (3) P ∨ (Q ∨ R) ∨ S   2,Assoc.
      (4) (Q ∨ R) ∨ P ∨ S   3,Comm.
      (5) (Q ∨ R) ∨ (~P ⊃ S)

                                     4,Impl.

      (6) Q ∨ [R ∨ (~P ⊃ S)]

                                     5,Assoc.

      (7) Q ∨ [~R ⊃ (~P ⊃ S)]

                                     6,Impl.

      (8) ~Q ⊃ [~R ⊃ (~P ⊃ S)]   7,Impl.

(C)   1   (1) M ⊃ F
        (2) K ⊃ I
        (3) B ∨ C
        (4) C ⊃ ~(F ∨ I)
        (5) ~B   /∴ ~M
        (6) C   3,5,DS
        (7) ~(F ∨ I)   4,6,MP
        (8) ~F . ~I   7,de M.
        (9) ~F   8,Simp.
      (10) ~M   1,9,MT
  2   (1) (S ∨ N) ⊃ R
        (2) A ⊃ F
        (3) N ⊃ ~A
        (4) ~F ⊃ ~R
        (5) ~(S ⊃ N)   /∴ F
        (6) ~(~S ∨ N)   5,Impl.
        (7) S . ~N   6,de M.,DN
        (8) S   7,Simp.
        (9) S ∨ N   8,Add.
      (10) R   1,9,MP
      (11) ~~R   10,DN
      (12) ~~F   4,11,MT
      (13) F   12,DN
  3   (1) X ⊃ S
        (2) F ⊃ X
        (3) K ⊃ ~X

    (4) X

                                /∴ ∼F ⊃ ∼K

    (5) X ⊃ ∼K   3,Trans.,DN

    (6) ∼K   4,5,MP

    (7) ∼K ∨ F   6,Add.

    (8) F ∨ ∼K   7,Comm.

    (9) ∼F ⊃ ∼K   8,Impl.

4 (1) M ⊃ (E . ∼I)

    (2) M ⊃ ∼N

    (3) N ⊃ I

    (4) N

                                  /∴ ∼I ⊃ ∼E

    (5) I   3,4,MP

    (6) I ∨ ∼E   5,Add.

    (7) ∼I ⊃ ∼E   6,Impl.

5 (1) (F ∨ W) ⊃ (D . I)

    (2) D ⊃ S

    (3) ∼S

                                    /∴ ∼F

    (4) ∼D   2,3,MT

    (5) ∼(D . I) ⊃ ∼(F ∨ W)   1,Trans.

    (6) (∼D ∨ ∼I) ⊃ ∼(F ∨ W)   5,de M.

    (7) (∼D ∨ ∼I) ⊃ (∼F . ∼W)   6,de M.

    (8) ∼D ∨ ∼I   4,Add.

    (9) ∼F . ∼W   7,8,MP

  (10) ∼F   9,Simp.

6 (1) W ⊃ G

    (2) C ⊃ T

    (3) G ⊃ (P . H)

    (4) T ⊃ (Q . U)

    (5) ∼Q

                                    /∴ ∼C

    (6) ∼(Q . U) ⊃ ∼T   4,Trans.

    (7) (∼Q ∨ ∼U) ⊃ ∼T   6,de M.

    (8) ∼Q ∨ ∼U   5,Add.

    (9) ∼T   7,8,MP

  (10) ∼C   2,9,MT

7 (1) (G . D) ⊃ ∼A

    (2) A ⊃ C

    (3) C ⊃ (S . F)

    (4) F ⊃ D

    (5) A

			/∴ ~G
	(6)	A ⊃ ~(G . D)	1,Trans.,DN
	(7)	~(G . D)	5,6,MP
	(8)	~G ∨ ~D	7,de M.
	(9)	~D ∨ ~G	8,Comm.
	(10)	C	2,5,MP
	(11)	S . F	3,10,MP
	(12)	F	11,Comm.Simp.
	(13)	D	4,12,MP
	(14)	~~D	13,DN
	(15)	~G	9,14,DS
8	(1)	(B ⊃ S) ⊃ A	
	(2)	K ∨ ~(H ⊃ W)	
	(3)	~A	
	(4)	O ⊃ (H ⊃ W)	
	(5)	(B ⊃ S) ∨ ~K	
			/∴ ~O
	(6)	~(B ⊃ S)	1,3,MT
	(7)	~K	5,6,DS
	(8)	~(H ⊃ W)	2,7,DS
	(9)	~O	4,8,MT
9	(1)	H ≡ (G ∨ B)	
	(2)	G ⊃ W	
	(3)	~W ⊃ S	
	(4)	G ⊃ C	
	(5)	B ⊃ W	
	(6)	~(C ⊃ W)	
			/∴ ~H
	(7)	~C . ~W	6,de M.
	(8)	~W	7,Comm.Simp.
	(9)	~G	2,8,MT
	(10)	~B	5,8,MT
	(11)	~G . ~B	9,10,Conj.
	(12)	~(G ∨ B)	11,de M.
	(13)	[H ⊃ (GrB)] . [(G ∨ B) ⊃ H]	
			1,Equiv.
	(14)	H ⊃ (G ∨ B)	13,Simp.
	(15)	~H	12,14,MT.
10	(1)	1 (P ∨ T) ⊃ (H ⊃ C)	
	(2)	(~ C ∨ A) ⊃ (P . H)	/ ∴ C
	(3)	~C	I.P.
	(4)	~C ∨ A	3,Add.

(5)	P . H	2,4,MP
(6)	P	5,Simp.
(7)	P ∨ T	6,Add.
(8)	H ⊃ C	1,7,MP
(9)	H	5,Comm,Simp.
(10)	C	8,9.MP
(11)	C .~C	10,3,Conj.

Part III

Section 1   page 139
Note that it does not matter what abbreviatory letters you use so
long as (i) you use the same letter for the same term and (ii) you
use different letters for different terms.

1   All S are E. All D are S. *So:* all D are E.
2   No R are E. Some R are C. *Therefore:* some C are not E.
3   No W is S. Some W is M. *So:* some M is not S.
4   All M are B. All B are A. *Therefore:* all M are A.
5   All T are W. Some T are R. *So:* some R are W.
6   If no S are V and all L are S, then no L are V.
7   All B are L. Some B are E. *So:* some E are L.
8   If no C are M and all D are C, then no D are M.
9   No B are F, and all B are C. *Therefore:* some C are not F.
10 If all A are C and some P are not C, then some P are not A.

The following pairs of arguments have the same form: 1 and
4, 2 and 3, 6 and 8.

Section 2   page 144
(A) 1   Dick is a lawyer.
     2   Tom is a doctor.
     3   The man with a scarred face is an Indian chief.
     4   Harry is a doctor.
     5   The man with a scarred face is a lawyer.
     6   Harry is an Indian chief.
(B) Use small letters for individual constants and capitals to
     abbreviate predicates:

     1   Sm   5   Pm
     2   Jg   6   Rg
     3   Lj   7   Rm . Bm
     4   Br

8 Rm . (Cm ∨ Bm)
9 Sb
10 Dt

Section 3   *page 149*

(A) 1 Fj
     2 Gc
     3 Dm
     4 Pc
     5 Lg
     6 Mq

(B) 1 (x)Cx
     2 (∃x)Dx
     3 (x) ∼Cx
     4 (∃x)Rx
     5 ∼(∃x)Dx
     6 (x)Ax
     7 (∃x) ∼Cx
     8 (∃x) ∼Ax
     1 and 7, 2 and 5, 6 and 8 are negations of each other.

(C) 1 (∃x)Rx
     2 (x)Ax
     3 ∼(x) ∼Rx
     4 (∃x) ∼Wx
     5 ∼(∃x) ∼Ax
     6 ∼(x)Wx
     1 and 3, 2 and 5, 4 and 6 are equivalent.

Section 4   *page 153*

(A) 1 (x)(Bx ⊃ Hx)
     2 (x)(Mx ⊃ Rx) *or* (∃x)(Mx . Rx) (depending on how
        you interpret 'Men are rational')
     3 (∃x)(Jx . Dx)
     4 (x)(Nx ⊃ ∼Ux)
     5 (∃x)(Cx . Ex)
     6 (∃x)(Sx . ∼Hx)
     7 (x)(Gx ⊃ Fx) (Note that we cannot use 'G' for *both*
        predicates)
     8 (∃x)Fx . ∼Gx) (Using 'Fx' for '*x* glitters')
     9 (x)(Ux ⊃ Px) (where 'U' = 'understands human moti-
        vation' and 'P' = 'is a psychologist')
     10 (∃x)(Ax . Rx)

(B)
1 $(\exists x)Mx$ or $\sim(x)\sim Mx$
2 $(x)Cx$ or $\sim(\exists x)\sim Cx$
3 $(x)(Hx \supset Mx)$ or $\sim(\exists x)(Hx . \sim Mx)$
4 $(x)(Ex \supset \sim Dx)$ or $\sim(\exists x)(Ex . Dx)$
5 $(\exists x)(Jx . Ux)$ or $\sim(x)(Jx \supset \sim Ux)$
6 $(\exists x)(Mx . Wx)$ or $\sim(x)(Mx \supset \sim Wx)$
7 $(x)(Hx \supset Vx)$ or $\sim(\exists x)(Hx . \sim Vx)$
8 $(\exists x)(Hx . Tx)$ or $\sim(x)(Hx \supset \sim Tx)$
9 $(x)\sim Px$ or $\sim(\exists x)Px$
10 $(x)(Ax \supset Px)$ or $\sim(\exists x)(Ax . \sim Px)$

Exercises on Part III *page 156*

1 $Dt . Ds$ (Where it is inconvenient to use the initials of proper names because they are identical, any distinguishing letters may be used as long as they are used consistently.)
2 $Bu . \sim Du$
3 $Ga . Cg$
4 $Dt \supset Ga$
5 $Bu . Gu$
6 $Dt \lor (x)(Dx \supset Bx)$
7 $(Dt . Ds) \supset Bu . p$
8 $(x)[(Dx \supset Hx) . Dm] \therefore Hm$
9 $(x)(Ix \supset \sim Dx) . (\exists x)(Px . Dx) \qquad \therefore (\exists x)(Px . Ix)$
10 $(x)(Rx \supset Ix) . (\exists x)(Rx . Fx) \qquad \therefore (\exists x)(Ix . Fx)$
11 $(x)(Nx \supset \sim Wx) . (\exists x)(Ax . Nx) \qquad \therefore (\exists x)(Ax . \sim Wx)$
12 $[(x)(Qx \supset \sim Vx) . (x)(Dx \supset Vx)] \therefore (x)(Dx \supset \sim Qx)$
13 $(x)(Px \supset Ex) . (\exists x)(Px . \sim Hx)$
14 $(x)[Lx \supset (Ix . Ex)]$
15 $(x)[(Sx \supset (Cx \lor Ax)]$
16 $(\exists x)[(Nx \lor Px) . Fx]$ (Notice that we cannot express, at this level of logic, the force of the word 'most' here.)
17 $(x)[(Cx \lor Ax) \supset Mx]$
18 $(x)(Ax \supset Ex) . (\exists x)(Ex.Rx) . \overline{(x)[(Rx \lor Ex) \supset Sx]}$
$$\therefore (\exists x)(Ax . Sx)$$

(*Note* that 'rare and expensive' in the third premiss is ambiguous in English. It can be read either as '$Rx \lor Ex$' or '$Rx . Ex$' since things can be and often are both rare and expensive. The case is different with examples 16 and 17 above.)

19 $(x)(Jx \supset Sx) . (x)[(Jx \lor Sx) \supset Ux]$
$$\therefore (x)[Jx \supset (Ux . Sx)]$$

20 $(x)[(Nx \lor Px) \supset Gx] . (x)(Gx \supset Fx) . (\exists x)(Px . Cx)$
$\therefore (\exists x)(Cx . Fx)$

Part IV   *page 167*

Section 2

1   (1) $(x)(Px \supset \sim Hx)$
    (2) $(x)(Mx \supset Px)$

                                                $\therefore (x)(Mx \supset \sim Hx)$
    (3) $Pz \supset \sim Hz$ 1,UI
    (4) $Mz \supset Pz$ 2,UI
    (5) $Mz \supset \sim Hz$ 3,4,HS
    (6) $(x)(Mx \supset \sim Hx)$ 5,UG

2   (1) $(x)(Bx \supset Dx)$
    (2) $(x)(Qx \supset Dx)$

                                                $\therefore (x)(Qx \supset Dx)$
    (3) $Bz \supset Dz$ 1,UI
    (4) $Qz \supset Bz$ 2,UI
    (5) $Qz \supset Dz$ 3,4,HS
    (6) $(x)(Qx \supset Dx)$ 5,UG

3   (1) $(x)(Ix \supset \sim Tx)$
    (2) $(x)(Cx \supset Tx)$

                                                $\therefore (x)(Cx \supset \sim Ix)$
    (3) $Iz \supset \sim Tz$ 1,UI
    (4) $Cz \supset Tz$ 2,UI
    (5) $Tz \supset \sim Iz$ 3,Trans.,DN
    (6) $Cz \supset \sim Iz$ 4,5,HS
    (7) $(x)(Cx \supset \sim Tx)$ 6,UG

4   (1) $(x)(Hx \supset Sx)$
    (2) $(x)(Sx \supset \sim Fx)$

                                                $\therefore (x)(Fx \supset \sim Hx)$
    (3) $Hz \supset Sz$ 1,UI
    (4) $Sz \supset \sim Fz$ 2,UI
    (5) $Hz \supset \sim Fz$ 3,4,HS
    (6) $Fz \supset \sim Hz$ 5,Trans.,DN
    (7) $(x)(Fx \supset \sim Hx)$ 6,UG

5   (1) $(x)[Dx \supset \sim(Fx \lor Cx)]$
    (2) $(x)(Bx \supset Dx)$

                                                $\therefore (x)(Bx \supset \sim Fx)$

(3)	$Dz \supset \sim(Fz \lor Cz)$	I,UI
(4)	$Bz \supset Dz$	2,UI
(5)	$\sim Dz \lor \sim(Fz \lor Cz)$	3,Impl.
(6)	$\sim Dz \lor (\sim Fz \cdot \sim Cz)$	5,de M.
(7)	$(\sim Dz \lor \sim Fz) \cdot (\sim Dz \lor \sim Cz)$	6,Distr.
(8)	$\sim Dz \lor \sim Fz$	7,Simp.
(9)	$Dz \supset \sim Fz$	8,Impl.
(10)	$Bz \supset \sim Fz$	4,9,HS
(11)	$(x)(Bx \supset \sim Fx)$	10,UG

6 (1) $(x)[(Ax \lor Tx) \supset Mx]$
   (2) $(x)[Mx \supset (Cx \cdot Hx)]$

$\therefore (x)(Tx \supset Hx)$

(3)	$(Az \lor Tz) \supset Mz$	1,UI
(4)	$Mz \supset (Cz \cdot Hz)$	2,UI
(5)	$\sim Mz \lor (Cz \cdot Hz)$	4,Impl.
(6)	$(\sim Mz \lor Cz) \cdot (\sim Mz \lor Hz)$	5,Distr.
(7)	$\sim Mz \lor Hz$	6,Comm.Simp.
(8)	$Mz \supset Hz$	7,Impl.
(9)	$\sim(Az \lor Tz) \lor Mz$	3,Impl.
(10)	$(\sim Az \cdot \sim Tz) \lor Mz$	8,de M.
(11)	$Mz \lor (\sim Az \cdot \sim Tz)$	10,Comm.
(12)	$(Mz \lor \sim Az) \cdot (Mz \lor \sim Tz)$	11,Distr.
(13)	$Mz \lor \sim Tz$	12,Comm.Simp.
(14)	$\sim Tz \lor Mz$	13,Comm.
(15)	$Tz \supset Mz$	14,Impl.
(16)	$Tz \supset Hz$	8,15,HS
(17)	$(x)(Tx \supset Hx)$	16,UG

7 (1) $(x)[Sx \supset (Rx \cdot Tx)]$
   (2) $(x)(Jx \supset \sim Rx)$

$\therefore (x)(Sx \supset \sim Jx)$

(3)	$Sz \supset (Rz \cdot Tz)$	I,UI
(4)	$Jz \supset \sim Rz$	2,UI
(5)	$\sim Sz \lor (Rz \cdot Tz)$	3,Impl.
(6)	$(\sim Sz \lor Rz) \cdot (\sim Sz \lor Tz)$	5,Distr.
(7)	$\sim Sz \lor Rz$	6,Simp.
(8)	$Sz \supset Rz$	7,Impl.
(9)	$Rz \supset \sim Jz$	4,Trans,DN.
(10)	$Sz \supset \sim Jz$	8,9,HS
(11)	$(x)(Sx \supset \sim Jx)$	10,UG

8 (1) $(x)[Mx \supset (Wx \cdot Ex)]$

$\therefore (x)(\sim Wx \supset \sim Mx)$

   (2) $Mz \supset (Wz \cdot Ez)$ I,UI

(3) $\sim Mz \lor (Wz . Ez)$ 2,Impl.
(4) $(\sim Mz \lor Wz) . (\sim Mz \lor Ez)$ 3,Distr.
(5) $\sim Mz \lor Wz$ 4,Simp.
(6) $Mz \supset Wz$ 5,Impl.
(7) $\sim Wz \supset \sim Mz$ 6,Trans.
(8) $(x)(\sim Wx \supset \sim Mx)$ 7,UG

9   (1) $(x)(Px \supset \sim Rx)$
     (2) $(x)[\sim Rx \supset (Ax . Dx)]$
     (3) $(x)(Dx \supset Sx)$

                           $\therefore (x)(Px \supset Sx)$

     (4) $Pz \supset \sim Rz$ 1,UI
     (5) $\sim Rz \supset (Az . Dz)$ 2,UI
     (6) $Dz \supset Sz$ 3,UI
     (7) $Pz \supset (Az . Dz)$ 4,5,HS
     (8) $\sim Pz \lor (Az . Dz)$ 7,Impl.
     (9) $(\sim Pz \lor Az) . (\sim Pz \lor Dz)$ 8,Distr.
   (10) $\sim PzI \lor Dz$ 9,Comm.Simp.
   (11) $Pz \supset Dz$ 10,Impl.
   (12) $Pz \supset Sz$ 6,11,HS
   (13) $(x)(Px \supset Sx)$ 12,UG

Section 3

page 171

1   (1) $(x)(Nx \supset \sim Ux)$
     (2) $(\exists x)(Ux . Ix)$

                           $\therefore (\exists x)(Ix . \sim Nx)$

     (3) $Ua . Ia$ 2,EI
     (4) $Na \supset \sim Ua$ I,UI
     (5) $Ua \supset \sim Na$ 4,Trans.,DN
     (6) Ua 3,Simp.
     (7) $\sim Na$ 5,6,MP
     (8) Ia 3,Comm.Simp.
     (9) $Ia . \sim Na$ 7,8,Conj.
   (10) $(\exists x)(Ix . \sim Nx)$ 9,EG

2   (1) $(x)(Rx \supset Ex)$
     (2) $(\exists x)(Px . \sim Ex)$

                           $\therefore (\exists x)(Px . \sim Rx)$

     (3) $Pa . \sim Ea$ 2,EI
     (4) $Ra \supset Ea$ I,UI
     (5) $\sim Ea \supset \sim Ra$ 4,Trans.
     (6) $\sim Ea$ 3,Comm.Simp.
     (7) $\sim Ra$ 5,6,MP
     (8) Pa 3,Simp.

   (9) Pa . ~Ra   7,8,Conj.
  (10) (∃x)(Px . ~Rx)   9,EG

3 (1) (x)(Bx ⊃ Lx)
    (2) (∃x)(Cx . Bx)

                          ∴ (∃x)(Cx . Lx)
    (3) Ca . Ba   2,EI
    (4) Ba ⊃ La   I,UI
    (5) Ba   3,Comm.Simp.
    (6) La   4,5,MP
    (7) Ca   3,Simp.
    (8) Ca . La   6,7,Comm.
    (9) (∃x)(Cx . Lx)   8,EG

4 (1) (x)(Rx ⊃ ~Sx)
    (2) (∃x)(Rx . Cx)

                          ∴ (∃x)(Cx . ~Sx)
    (3) Ra . Ca   2,EI
    (4) Ra ⊃ ~Sa   1,UI
    (5) Ra   3,Simp.
    (6) ~Sa   4,5,MP
    (7) Ca   3,Comm.Simp.
    (8) Ca . ~Sa   6,7,Conj.
    (9) (∃x)(Cx . ~Sx)   8,EG

5 (1) (x)(Nx ⊃ ~Wx)
    (2) (∃x)(Ax . Nx)

                          ∴ (∃x)(Ax . ~Wx)
    (3) Aa . Na   2,EI
    (4) Na ⊃ ~Wa   I,UI
    (5) Na   3,Comm.Simp.
    (6) ~Wa   4,5,MP
    (7) Aa   3,Simp.
    (8) Aa . ~Wa   6,7,Conj.
    (9) (∃x)(Ax . ~Wx)   8,EG

6 (1) (x)(Tx ⊃ Wx)
    (2) (∃x)(Tx . Rx)

                          ∴ (∃x)(Rx . Wx)
    (3) Ta . Ra   2,EI
    (4) Ta ⊃ Wa   I,UI
    (5) Ta   3,Simp.
    (6) Wa   4,5,MP
    (7) Ra   3,Comm.Simp.
    (8) Ra . Wa   6,7,Conj.
    (9) (∃x)(Rx . Wx)   8,EG

7   (1) $(x)(Ex \supset Dx)$
    (2) $(\exists x)(Px . \sim Dx)$

                     ∴ $(\exists x)(Px . \sim Ex)$
    (3) $Pa . \sim Da$ 2,EI
    (4) $Ea \supset Da$ I,UI
    (5) $\sim Da \supset \sim Ea$ 4,Trans.
    (6) $\sim Da$ 3,Comm.Simp.
    (7) $\sim Ea$ 5,6,MP
    (8) Pa 3,Simp.
    (9) $Pa . \sim Ea$ 7,8,Conj.
  (10) $(\exists x)(Px . \sim Ex)$ 9,EG

8   (1) $(\exists x)(Cx . Px . Dx)$
    (2) $(x)(Px \supset Ix)$

                     ∴ $(\exists x)(Cx . Ix)$
    (3) $Ca . Pa . Da$ 1,EI
    (4) $Pa \supset Ia$ 2,UI
    (5) $Ca . (Pa . Da)$ 3,Assoc.
    (6) $(Pa . Da) . Ca$ 5,Comm.
    (7) $Pa . (Da . Ca)$ 6,Assoc.
    (8) Pa 7,Simp.
    (9) Ia 4,8,MP
  (10) Ca 5,Simp.
  (11) $Ca . Ia$ 9,10,Conj.
  (12) $(\exists x)(Cx . Ix)$ 11,EG

9   (1) $(x)(Mx \supset \sim Ex)$
    (2) $(x)(\sim Hx \supset Ex)$
    (3) Mt

                     ∴ Ht
    (4) $Mt \supset \sim Et$ 1,UI
    (5) $\sim Ht \supset Et$ 2,UI
    (6) $\sim Et \supset Ht$ 5,Trans.,DN
    (7) $Mt \supset Ht$ 4,6,HS
    (8) Ht 3,7,MP

10 (1) Gs
    (2) $(x)(Gx \supset Lx)$
    (3) $(x)(Lx \supset \sim Bx)$

                     ∴ $\sim Bs$
    (4) $Gs \supset Ls$ 2,UI
    (5) $Ls \supset \sim Bs$ 3,UI
    (6) $Gs \supset \sim Bs$ 4,5,HS
    (7) $\sim Bs$ 1,6,MP

1   (1) $(x)(Px \supset \sim Fx)$
     (2) $(\exists x)(Fx \cdot Vx)$

                                        $\therefore (\exists x)(Vx \cdot \sim Px)$
     (3) $Fa \cdot Va$ 2,EI
     (4) $Pa \supset \sim Fa$ 1,UI
     (5) Fa 3,Simp.
     (6) $\sim\sim Fa$ 5,DN
     (7) $\sim Pa$ 4,6,MT
     (8) Va 3,Comm.Simp.
     (9) $Va \cdot \sim Pa$ 7,8,Conj.
     (10) $(\exists x)(Vx \cdot \sim Px)$ 9,EG

2   (1) $(x)[(Lx \lor Cx) \supset Mx]$
     (2) $(\exists x)(Lx \cdot Sx)$
     (3) $(\exists x)(Lx \cdot Zx)$
     (4) $(x)(Mx \supset Zx)$

                                        $\therefore (\exists x)(Sx \cdot Zx)$
     (5) $La \cdot Sa$ 2,EI
     (6) La 5,Simp.
     (7) $La \lor Ca$ 6,Add.
     (8) $(La \lor Ca) \supset Ma$ 1,UI
     (9) Ma 7,8,MP
     (10) $Ma \supset Za$ 4,UI
     (11) Za 9,10,MP
     (12) Sa 5,Comm.Simp.
     (13) $Sa \cdot Za$ 11,12,Conj.
     (14) $(\exists x)(Sx \cdot Zx)$ 13,EG

3   (1) $(x)(Jx \supset Dx)$
     (2) $(\exists x)(Hx \cdot \sim Dx)$

                                        $\therefore (\exists x)(Hx \cdot \sim Jx)$
     (3) $Ha \cdot \sim Da$ 2,EI
     (4) $Ja \supset Da$ 1,UI
     (5) $\sim Da \supset \sim Ja$ 4,Trans.
     (6) $\sim Da$ 3,Comm.Simp.
     (7) $\sim Ja$ 5,6,MP
     (8) Ha 3,Simp.
     (9) $Ha \cdot \sim Ja$ 7,8,Conj.
     (10) $(\exists x)(Hx \cdot \sim Jx)$ 9,EG

4   (1) $(x)(Sx \supset \sim Vx)$
     (2) $(x)(Lx \supset Sx)$

                                        $\therefore (x)(Lx \supset \sim Vx)$
     (3) $Sz \supset \sim Vz$ 1,UI

(4)	Lz ⊃ Sz	2,UI
(5)	Lz ⊃ ∼Vz	3,4,HS
(6)	(x)(Lx ⊃ ∼Vx)	5,UG
5 (1)	(x)(Dx ⊃ Cx)	
(2)	(∃x)(Dx . Ex)	
(3)	(x)[(Cx . Ex) ⊃ Px]	
		∴ (∃x)(Dx . Px)
(4)	Da . Ea	2,EI
(5)	Da ⊃ Ca	1,UI
(6)	(Ca . Ea) ⊃ Pa	3,UI
(7)	Da	4,Simp.
(8)	Ca	5,7,MP
(9)	Ea	4,Comm.Simp.
(10)	Ca . Ea	8,9,Conj.
(11)	Pa	6,10,MP
(12)	Da . Pa	7,11,Conj.
(13)	(∃x)(Dx . Px)	12,EG
6 (1)	(x)(Px ⊃ Lx)	
(2)	(x)[(Lx . Px) ⊃ Sx]	
		∴ (x)[Px ⊃ (Lx . Sx)]
(3)	Pz ⊃ Lz	1,UI
(4)	(Lz . Pz) ⊃ Sz	2,UI
(5)	Lz ⊃ (Pz ⊃ Sz)	4,Exp
(6)	Pz ⊃ (Pz ⊃ Sz)	3,5,HS
(7)	(Pz . Pz) ⊃ Sz	6,Exp.
(8)	Pz ⊃ Sz	7,Taut.
(9)	(Pz ⊃ Lz) . (Pz ⊃ Sz)	3,8,Conj.
(10)	(∼Pz ∨ Lz) . (∼Pz ∨ Sz)	9,Impl.
(11)	∼Pz ∨ (Lz . Sz)	10,Distr.
(12)	Pz ⊃ (Lz . Sz)	11,Impl.
(13)	(x)[Px ⊃ (Lx . Sx)]	12,UG
7 (1)	(x)[(Hx . Bx) ⊃ (Wx . Cx)]	
(2)	(x)[(Hx . Ex) ⊃ Bx]	
		∴ (x)[(Hx . Ex) ⊃ Wx]
(3)	(Hz . Bz) ⊃ (Wz . Cz)	1,UI
(4)	(Hz . Ez) ⊃ Bz	2,UI
(5)	(Bz . Hz) ⊃ (Wz . Cz)	3,Comm.
(6)	Bz ⊃ [Hz ⊃ (Wz . Cz)]	5,Exp.
(7)	(Hz . Ez) ⊃ [Hz ⊃ (Wz . Cz)]	4,6,HS
(8)	[Hz . (Ez . Hz)] ⊃ [Wz . Cz]	7,Exp.
(9)	[(Hz . Hz) . Ez] ⊃ (Wz . Cz)	8,Assoc.Comm.

(10)	$(Hz . Ez) \supset (Wz . Cz)$	9,Taut.
(11)	$\sim(Hz . Ez) \lor (Wz . Cz)$	10,Impl.
(12)	$[\sim(Hz . Ez) \lor Wz] . [\sim(Hz . Ez) \lor Cz]$	
		11,Distr.
(13)	$\sim(Hz . Ez) \lor Wz$	12,Simp.
(14)	$(Hz . Ez) \supset Wz$	13,Impl.
(15)	$(x)(Hx . Ex) \supset Wx$	14,UG

8

(1)	$(x)[Tx \supset (Fx . Dx)]$	
(2)	$(\exists x)(Ex . Tx)$	
		$\therefore (\exists x)(Ex . Dx)$
(3)	$Ea . Ta$	2,EI
(4)	$Ta \supset (Fa . Da)$	1,UI
(5)	Ta	3,Comm.Simp.
(6)	$Fa . Da$	4,5,MP
(7)	Ea	3,Simp.
(8)	Da	6,Comm.Simp.
(9)	$Ea . Da$	7,8,Conj.
(10)	$(\exists x)(Ex . Dx)$	9,EG

9

(1)	$(x)[(Bx \lor Gx) \supset Fx]$	
(2)	$(x)[(Fx \lor Vx) \supset Nx]$	
		$\therefore (x)(Bx \supset Nx)$
(3)	$(Bz \lor Gz) \supset Fz$	1,UI
(4)	$(Fz \lor Vz) \supset Nz$	2,UI
(5)	$\sim(Bz \lor Gz) \lor Fz$	3,Impl.
(6)	$(\sim Bz . \sim Gz) \lor Fz$	5,de M.
(7)	$Fz \lor (\sim Bz . \sim Gz)$	6,Comm.
(8)	$(Fz \lor \sim Bz) . (Fz \lor \sim Gz)$	7,Distr.
(9)	$Fz \lor \sim Bz$	8,Simp.
(10)	$Bz \supset Fz$	9,Comm.Impl.
(11)	$\sim(Fz \lor Vz) \lor Nz$	4,Impl.
(12)	$(\sim Fz . \sim Vz) \lor Nz$	11,de M.
(13)	$Nz \lor (\sim Fz . \sim Vz)$	12,Comm.
(14)	$(Nz \lor \sim Fz) . (Nz \lor \sim Vz)$	13,Distr.
(15)	$Nz \lor \sim Fz$	14,Simp.
(16)	$Fz \supset Nz$	15,Comm.,Impl.
(17)	$Bz \supset Nz$	10,16,HS
(18)	$(x)Bx \supset Nx$	17,UG

10

(1)	$(x)[Cx \supset (Fx \lor Kx)]$	
(2)	$(x)(Fx \supset Nx)$	
(3)	$(\exists x)(Cx . \sim Nx)$	
		$\therefore (\exists x)(Cx . Kx)$
(4)	$Ca . \sim Na$	3,EI

(5)	$Ca \supset (Fa \lor Ka)$	1,UI
(6)	$Fa \supset Na$	2,UI
(7)	Ca	4,Simp.
(8)	$Fa \lor Ka$	5,7,MP
(9)	$\sim Na$	4,Comm.Simp.
(10)	$\sim Fa$	6,9,MT
(11)	Ka	8,10,DS
(12)	$Ca \,.\, Ka$	7,11,Conj.
(13)	$(\exists x)(Cx \,.\, Kx)$	

Section 5   *page 179*

1 (1) $(x)(Dx \supset \sim Fx)$
   (2) $(x)(Dx \supset Bx)$

                                            $\therefore (\exists x)(Bx \,.\, \sim Fx)$
   *(3) $(\exists x)(Dx)$ Assumption of existence
   (4) Da 3,EI
   (5) $Da \supset \sim Fa$ 1,UI
   (6) $Da \supset Ba$ 2,UI
   (7) $\sim Fa$ 4,5,MP
   (8) Ba 2,4,MP
   (9) $Ba \,.\, \sim Fa$ 7,8,Conj.
   (10) $(\exists x)(Bx \,.\, \sim Fx)$ 9,EG

2 (1) $(x)(Px \supset Nx)$
   (2) $(x)(Px \supset Cx)$

                                            $\therefore (\exists x)(Nx \,.\, Cx)$
   *(3) $(\exists x)Px$ Assumption of existence
   (4) Pa 3,EI
   (5) $Pa \supset Na$ 1,UI
   (6) $Pa \supset Ca$ 2,UI
   (7) Na 4,5,MP
   (8) Ca 4,6,MP
   (9) $Na \,.\, Ca$ 7,8,Conj.
   (10) $(\exists x)(Nx \,.\, Cx)$ 9,EG

3 (1) $(x)(Px \supset \sim Mx)$
   (2) $(x)(Mx \supset Tx)$

                                            $\therefore (\exists x)(Tx \,.\, \sim Px)$
   *(3) $(\exists x)Mx$
   (4) Ma 3,EI
   (5) $Pa \supset \sim Ma$ 1,UI
   (6) $Ma \supset Ta$ 2,UI
   (7) Ta 4,6,MP
   (8) $\sim\sim Ma$ 4,DN

	(9)	$\sim Pa$	5,8,MT
	(10)	$Ta . \sim Pa$	7,9,Conj.
	(11)	$(\exists x)(Tx . \sim Px)$	10,EG
4	(1)	$(x)((Fx \lor Vx) \supset Nx)$	
	(2)	$(x)(Nx \supset Px)$	
	(3)	$(x)(Px \supset Dx)$	
			$/ \therefore (\exists x)(Vx . Dx)$
*	(4)	$(\exists x)Vx$	
	(5)	Va	4,EI
	(6)	$(Fa \lor Va) \supset Na$	1,UI
	(7)	$Fa \lor Va$	5,Add.Comm.
	(8)	Na	6,7,MP
	(9)	$Na \supset Pa$	2,UI
	(10)	Pa	8,9,MP
	(11)	$Pa \supset Da$	3,UI
	(12)	Da	10,11,MP
	(13)	$Va . Da$	5,12,Conj.
	(14)	$(\exists x)(Vx . Dx)$	13,EG
5	(1)	$(x)[(Fx \lor Tx \lor Sx) \supset Ax]$	
	(2)	$(x)(Ax \supset Hx)$	
			$/ \therefore (\exists x)(Hx . Sx)$
*	(3)	$(\exists x)Sx$	
	(4)	Sa	3,EI
	(5)	$(Fa \lor Ta \lor Sa) \supset Aa$	1,UI
	(6)	$Aa \supset Ha$	2,UI
	(7)	$(Sa \lor Fa \lor Ta) \supset Aa$	5,Assoc.Comm.
	(8)	$\sim(Sa \lor Fa \lor Ta) \lor Aa$	7,Impl.
	(9)	$(\sim Sa . \sim Fa . \sim Ta) \lor Aa$	8,de M.
	(10)	$Aa \lor (\sim Sa . \sim Fa . \sim Ta)$	9,Comm.
	(11)	$(Aa \lor \sim Sa) . (Aa \lor \sim Fa) . (Aa \lor \sim Ta)$	10 Dist.
	(12)	$(\sim Sa \lor Aa)$	11,Simp.Comm.
	(13)	$Sa \supset Aa$	12,Impl.
	(14)	Aa	4,13,MP
	(15)	Ha	6,14,MP
	(16)	$Ha . Sa$	4,15,Conj.
	(17)	$[\exists x)(Rx . Sx)$	16,EG

Exercises on Part IV

page 182

1	(1)	$(\exists x)(Vx . Tx)$
	(2)	$(x)(Tx \supset Ix)$

(3) $(x)[(Vx . Ix) \supset Hx]$
(4) $(x)(Hx \supset Lx)$

/∴ $(\exists x)(Vx . Lx)$

(5)	$Va . Ta$	1,EI
(6)	$Ta \supset Ia$	2,UI
(7)	$(Va . Ia) \supset Ha$	3,UI
(8)	$Ha \supset La$	4,UI
(9)	Ta	5,Comm.Simp.
(10)	Ia	6,9,MP
(11)	Va	5,Simp.
(12)	$Va . Ia$	10,11,Conj.
(13)	Ha	12,7,MP
(14)	La	8,13,MP
(15)	$Va . La$	13,14,Conj.
(16)	$(\exists x)(Vx . Lx)$	15,EG

2   (1) $(x)[(Vx \lor Wx) \supset Bx]$
    (2) $(x)[Bx \supset \sim(Sx \lor Gx)]$
    (3) $(\exists x)(Wx . Dx . Ux)$
    (4) $(\exists x)(Vx . \sim Ax)$
    (5) $(x)(Bx \supset Ax)$
    (6) $(x)[(Vx . Ux) \supset \sim Gx]$

∴ $(\exists x(Vx . Sx)$

(7)	$Va . \sim Aa$	4,EI
(8)	$(Va \lor Wa) \supset Ba$	1,UI
(9)	$Va \lor Wa$	7,Simp.Add.
(10)	Ba	8,9,MP
(11)	$Ba \supset Aa$	5,UI
(12)	Aa	10,11,MP

(At this point, it is clear that we have a contradiction. Compare 7 and 12. We can therefore prove *any* conclusion we wish. See p. 128.)

(13)	$Aa \lor (Va . Sa)$	11,Add.
(14)	$\sim Aa$	7,Comm.Simp.
(15)	$Va . Sa$	13,14,DS
(16)	$(\exists x)(Vx . Sx)$	15,EG

3   (1) $(x)[Vx \supset (Cx . Fx)]$
    (2) $(x)[Fx \supset (Ox \lor Ax \lor Bx)]$
    (3) $(x)[Vx \supset \sim(Ox \lor Ax)]$
    (4) $(x)(Bx \supset Kx)$
    (5) $(x)(Vx \supset \sim Kx)$

/∴ $(x) \sim Vx$

(6) $Vz \supset (Cz . Fz)$ 1,UI
(7) $Fz \supset (Oz \lor Az \lor Bz)$

                 2,UI
(8) $Vz \supset \sim(Oz \lor Az)$ 3,UI
(9) $Bz \supset Kz$ 4,UI
(10) $Vz \supset \sim Kz$ 5,UI
(11) $\sim Vz \lor (Cz . Fz)$ 6,Impl.
(12) $(\sim Vz \lor Cz) . (\sim Vz \lor Fz)$

                 11,Dist.
(13) $\sim Vz \lor Fz$ 12,Comm.Simp.
(14) $Vz \supset Fz$ 13,Impl.
(15) $Vz \supset (Oz \lor Az \lor Bz)$

                 7,14,HS

(16) Vz CP
(17) $Oz \lor Az \lor Bz$ 15,16,MP
(18) $(Oz \lor Az) \lor Bz$ 17,Assoc.
(19) $\sim(Oz \lor Az)$ 8,16,MP
(20) Bz
(21) $Vz \supset Bz$ 16-20,CP
(22) $Vz \supset Kz$ 9,21,HS
(23) $Kz \supset \sim Vz$ 10,Trans.,DN
(24) $Vz \supset \sim Vz$ 22,23,HS
(25) $\sim Vz \lor \sim Vz$ 24,Impl.
(26) $\sim Vz$ 25,Taut.
(27) $(x) \sim Vx$ 26,UG

(Remember that '$(x) \sim Vx$' is equivalent to: '$\sim(\exists x)Vx$'.)

4   (1) $(x)[(Sx \lor Gx) \supset Vx]$
        (2) $(\exists x)(Ix . Gx)$
        (3) $(\exists x)(Sx . Px)$
        (4) $(x)(Vx \supset \sim Ix)$
        (5) $(\exists x)(Sx . Fx)$

                     $(\exists x)(Px . Fx)$
       (6) $Ia . Ga$ 2,EI
       (7) $(Sa \lor Ga) \supset Va$ 1,UI
       (8) $Sa \lor Ga$ 6,Comm.Simp.Add.Comm.
       (9) Va 7,8,MP
    (10) $Va \supset \sim Ia$ 4,UI
    (11) $\sim Ia$ 9,10MP
    (12) Ia 6,Simp.

    (13) I*a* ∨ (P*a* . F*a*)   12,Add.
    (14) P*a* . F*a*   11,13,DS
    (15) (∃*x*)(P*x* . F*x*)   14,EG

5   (1) (*x*)[W*x* ⊃ (N*x* ∨ F*x*)]
    (2) (*x*)[(W*x* . N*x*) ⊃ ∼F*x*]
    (3) (∃*x*)(W*x* . F*x*)

                  ∴ (∃*x*)(W*x* . ∼N*x*)

    (4) W*a* . F*a*   3,EI
    (5) W*a* ⊃ (N*a* ∨ F*a*) 1,UI
    (6) (W*a* . N*a*) ⊃ ∼F*a* 2,UI
    (7) W*a*   4,Simp.
    (8) W*a* ⊃ (N*a* ⊃ ∼F*a*) 6,Exp.
    (9) N*a* ⊃ ∼F*a*   7,8,MP
    (10) F*a* ⊃ ∼N*a*   9,Trans,DN
    (11) F*a*   4,Comm.Simp.
    (12) ∼N*a*   10,11,MP
    (13) W*a* . ∼N*a*   7,12,Conj.
    (14) (∃*x*)(W*x* . ∼N*x*) 13,EG

6   (1) (*x*)[(W*x* ∨ H*x*) ⊃ (P*x* ∨ F*x*)]
    (2) (*x*)(F*x* ⊃ U*x*)
    (3) (∃*x*)(M*x* . H*x*)
    (4) (*x*)(M*x* ⊃ ∼P*x*)

                  ∴ (∃*x*)(M*x* . U*x*)

    (5) M*a* . H*a*   3,EI
    (6) M*a*   5,Simp.
    (7) M*a* ⊃ ∼P*a*   4,UI
    (8) (W*a* ∨ H*a*) ⊃ (P*a* ∨ F*a*)
                  1,UI
    (9) H*a*   5,Comm.Simp.
    (10) W*a* ∨ H*a*   9,Add.Comm.
    (11) P*a* ∨ F*a*   8,10,MP
    (12) ∼P*a*   6,7,MP
    (13) F*a*   11,12,DS
    (14) F*a* ⊃ U*a*   2,UI
    (15) U*a*   13,14,MP
    (16) M*a* . U*a*   6,15,Conj.
    (17) (∃*x*)(M*x* . U*x*) 16,EG

7   (1) (*x*)[(V*x* ∨ W*x*) ⊃ D*x*]
    (2) (*x*)(D*x* ⊃ O*x*)
    (3) (*x*)(R*x* ⊃ ∼O*x*)
    (4) (∃*x*)V*x*

                  ∴ (*x*)(W*x* ⊃ ∼R*x*)

	(5)	$(Vz \lor Wz) \supset Dz$	1,UI
	(6)	$Dz \supset Oz$	2,UI
	(7)	$Rz \supset \sim Oz$	3,UI
	(8)	$\sim(Vz \lor Wz) \lor Dz$	5,Impl.
	(9)	$(\sim Vz . \sim Wz) \lor Dz$	8,de M.
	(10)	$Dz \lor (\sim Vz . \sim Wz)$	9,Comm.
	(11)	$(Dz \lor \sim Vz) . (Dz \lor \sim Wz)$	10,Distr.
	(12)	$Dz \lor \sim Wz$	11,Comm.Simp.
	(13)	$Wz \supset Dz$	12,Comm.Impl.
	(14)	$Wz \supset Oz$	6,13,HS
	(15)	$Oz \supset \sim Rz$	7,Trans.,DN
	(16)	$Wz \supset \sim Rz$	14,15,HS
	(17)	$(x)(Wx \supset \sim Rx)$	16,UG

8

	(1)	$(x)(Wx \supset Ax)$	
	(2)	$(x)[Ax \supset (Ux . Ix)]$	
	(3)	$(x)(\sim Ix \supset Rx)$	
	(4)	$(x)(Ux \supset Dx)$	
	(5)	$(x)(Wx \supset \sim Dx)$	
			$\therefore (x) \sim Wx$
	(6)	$Wz \supset Az$	1,UI
	(7)	$Az \supset (Uz . Iz)$	2,UI
	(8)	$\sim Iz \supset Rz$	3,UI
	(9)	$Uz \supset Dz$	4,UI
	(10)	$Wz \supset \sim Dz$	5,UI
	(11)	$Wz \supset (Uz . Iz)$	6,7,HS
	(12)	$\sim Wz \lor (Uz . Iz)$	11,Impl.
	(13)	$(\sim Wz \lor Uz) . (\sim Wz \lor Iz)$	12,Distr.
	(14)	$Wz \supset Uz$	13,Simp.Impl.
	(15)	$Wz \supset Dz$	9,14,HS
	(16)	$Dz \supset \sim Wz$	10,Trans.,DN
	(17)	$Wz \supset \sim Wz$	15,16,HS
	(18)	$\sim Wz \lor \sim Wz$	17,Impl.
	(19)	$\sim Wz$	18,Taut.
	(20)	$(x) \sim Wx$	19,UG

9

	(1)	$(x)[Px \supset (Lx \lor Mx \lor Fx)]$	
	(2)	$(x)(Cx \supset Px)$	
	(3)	$(x)[(Cx \supset \sim(Lx \lor Mx)]$	
			$\therefore (x)(Cx \supset Fx)$
	(4)	$Pz \supset (Lz \lor Mz \lor Fz)$	1,UI

(5) $Cz \supset \sim(Lz \lor Mz)$ 2,UI
(6) $Cz \supset Pz$ 3,UI
(7) Cz CP
(8) $\sim(Lz \lor Mz)$ 5,7,MP
(9) $Cz \supset (Lz \lor Mz \lor Fz)$
       4,6,HS
(10) $(Lz \lor Mz) \lor Fz$ 7,9,MP, Assoc.
(11) Fz 8,10,HS
(12) $Cz \supset Fz$ 7-11,CP
(13) $(x)(Cx \supset Fx)$ 12,UG

10   (1) $(x)[Tx \supset (Fx \cdot Rx)]$
      (2) $(x)(Rx \supset Ox)$
      (3) $(\exists x)(Tx \cdot \sim Vx)$
      (4) $(x)[Fx \supset (Vx \lor Ix)]$
      (5) $(x)[Ox \supset (Px \lor Vx)]$
                       $\therefore (\exists x)(Px \cdot Ix)$

(6) $Ta \cdot \sim Va$ 3,EI
(7) $Ta \supset (Fa \cdot Ra)$ 1,UI
(8) $Ra \supset Oa$ 2,UI
(9) $Fa \supset (Va \lor Ia)$ 4,UI
(10) $Oa \supset (Pa \lor Va)$ 5,UI
(11) Ta 6,Simp.
(12) $Fa \cdot Ra$ 7,11,MP
(13) Fa 12,Simp.
(14) $Va \lor Ia$ 9,13,MP
(15) Ra 12,Comm.Simp.
(16) $Ra \supset (Pa \lor Va)$ 8,10,HS
(17) $Pa \lor Va$ 15,16,MP
(18) $\sim Va$ 6,Comm.Simp.
(19) Pa 17,Comm.18,DS
(20) Ia 14,18,DS
(21) $Pa \cdot Ia$ 19,20,Conj.
(22) $(\exists x)(Px \cdot Ix)$ 21,EG

Appendix:

Alternative Notations in Modern Logic

The symbolism used in this book is fairly standard in contemporary logic and is derived from Russell and Whitehead's classical *Principia Mathematica*, which appeared in 1910. However, several variant notations are in use and it is useful for the student to be aware of these, or at least, of the commonest of them.

Most of them differ little from the symbolism of this book and consist in alternative signs for the logical constants and the quantifiers. For example:

Negation: This can be written as '—' or '$\neg$' or as a stroke above the propositional sign, thus: $\bar{p} \vee \bar{q}$.

Conjunction: Instead of the dot sign, the following are sometimes used: & or $\wedge$.

Implication: Instead of the hook sign, some authors use an arrow: $\rightarrow$

Equivalence: Instead of the three bars, we sometimes find a double arrow: $\leftrightarrow$

The universal quantifier: We sometimes find: $(\forall x)$ in place of (x).

Thus the expressions: $\sim p \supset (q \vee r)$ and $(p . q) \equiv \sim r$ may appear as: $-p \rightarrow (q \vee r)$ and $(p \ \& \ q) \leftrightarrow -r$. And:

$$(x)(Fx \supset Gx)$$

may be written: $(\forall x)(Fx \rightarrow Gx)$.

But the most radically different notation in common use is the so-called Polish notation introduced by the late Professor Łuka-siewicz. In this symbolism, the constants *precede* the propositional signs that they govern and are represented by capital letters, thus:

Russell–Whitehead	*Polish*
$\sim p$	Np
$p \vee q$	Apq
$p \cdot q$	Kpq
$p \supset q$	Cpq
$p \equiv q$	Epq

Thus, the expression: $\sim p \supset (q \vee r)$, in our notation, becomes

CNpAqr

Although the Polish notation is more difficult to handle for beginning students, it has obvious advantages once it becomes familiar. In particular, no brackets are required. Quantifiers are represented as follows:

The universal quantifier becomes the Greek capital pi, Π and the existential quantifier becomes the Greek capital sigma, Σ. Predicate signs are usually lower case Greek letters. Thus:

$$(x)\mathrm{F}x \text{ becomes } \Pi x \phi x$$
$$(\exists x)\mathrm{F}x \text{ becomes } \Sigma x \phi x$$
$$(x)(\mathrm{F}x \supset \mathrm{G}x) \text{ becomes } \Pi x \mathrm{C} \phi x \psi x$$
$$(\exists x)(\mathrm{F}x \cdot \mathrm{G}x) \text{ becomes } \Sigma x \mathrm{K} \phi x \psi x$$

Notes on Further Reading

1   Peter Alexander: *Introduction to Logic* (London, 1969).
    This is a very readable text-book which moves gradually from
    ordinary language to logical symbolism and explains carefully
    the connections between the two.

2   Alice Ambrose and Morris Lazerowitz: *Fundamentals of
    Symbolic Logic* (New York, 1948).
    Though published thirty years ago, this is an excellent student
    book, a clear and systematic introduction which is still well
    worth study.

3   I. M. Copi: *Symbolic Logic* (Fifth Edition) (New York, 1977).
    This is a classic text-book of logic, now in its fifth edition.
    Almost all logic text-books published since 1954, including
    this one, owe much to it.

4   Alan Foster and Graham Shute: *Propositional Logic: A
    Student Introduction* (University of Aston, 1976).
    An excellent introduction to the logic of propositions. It is
    especially useful in having an abundance of exercises with
    solutions.

5   W. A. Hodges: *Logic* (London, 1977).
    This is a recent Pelican book. It is an orginal and elegant
    treatment but very difficult for any beginner who is not a
    natural logician. No one without mathematical tastes and
    skills is likely to find it a useful introduction.

6 E. J. Lemmon: *Beginning Logic* (London, 1965).
This is a widely used text-book, written clearly and concisely.

7 W. V. O. Quine: *Methods of Logic* (Second Edition) (London, 1962).
A famous book by one of the great logicians of the twentieth century. It is not easy reading but is well worth study.

8 B. Tapscott: *Elementary Applied Symbolic Logic* (New York, 1977). A clear and systematic text-book. It is less thorough than (3) but for that reason, easier for the elementary student.

Index

HOW YOUR MIND WORKS

DAVID COX

Jung found that a 'sense of meaning in life' was essential to human health, happiness and even security. In the first half of life, meaning is concerned with the establishment of the ego, the fulfilment of biological needs and duties and the achievement of a place in the world. In the second half of life the sphere of meaning shifts to the goal of inner understanding.

The aim of this book is to introduce Jung's ideas and his analysis of the structural aspects of the psyche. These views are given perspective by an initial consideration of other contemporary theories but the central theme is the same as that which ran through Jung's life and work, a concern for the spiritual nature of man and his need for self-knowledge.

David Cox has on two occasions been Chairman of the Guild of Pastoral Psychology and is at present Vicar of St Thomas' Southborough.

TEACH YOURSELF BOOKS

PHILOSOPHY: AN INTRODUCTION

ANTONY FLEW

This book introduces the beginner to the work of the major philosophers, presenting and discussing their ideas.

Written in clear, non-technical language it covers all the main areas of philosophy. It concentrates on those aspects most likely to be of immediate interest to contemporary readers such as the questions of morality, democracy and equality.

Antony Flew is Professor and Head of Department of Philosophy at the University of Reading.

TEACH YOURSELF BOOKS

ARITHMETIC

L. C. PASCOE

A basic course in arithmetic, fully decimalised and metri-
cated, this book has been designed to give the reader a
practical working knowledge of the subject.

Progressing from the elementary processes, the basic
aspects of arithmetic are comprehensively covered, with
detailed advice as to how, for example, percentages, simple
and compound interest, arithmetical graphs and statistics
can be of practical help to such problems as Income Tax,
rates and investment. Throughout the book, numerous
working examples are given in order to explain fully the
arithmetical processes involved.

TEACH YOURSELF BOOKS